HAIR
COLOUR & STYLES

Ellen Bolz
Edited by Anthea Bain

foulsham
LONDON • NEW YORK • TORONTO • SYDNEY

foulsham

The Publishing House, Bennetts Close,
Cippenham, Berkshire, SL1 5AP, England.

ISBN 0 572 02052 -X

This English language edition © 1996 W. Foulsham & Co. Ltd.,
Originally published by Falken-Verlag, GmbH, Niedernhausen TS, Germany
Photographs copyright © Falken-Verlag

Printed in Great Britain by Cambus Litho, East Kilbride.

What is a hair 'type' and what does it mean? – that you fit a particular look, or that you are unique? Neither – it is a combination of both. After all, everyone has certain characteristics: red or black hair, thick or fine, straight or curly. Everyone has their own taste, which predetermines the styles they will choose. Indeed, everyone has their own lifestyle which can determine what colour their hair should be - high or low maintenance? And which 'season' colour do your suit?

Apart from current fashion trends your hairstyle can usually be classified as 'sporty', 'classic', 'fun' or 'elegant'. These groups are used in this book to point you in a certain direction, but are vague enough to allow lots of scope within each area. This is to ensure that your individuality is not lost, and that you need not choose a style that is different at any price. Making the most of your hair has never been so easy.

Each style featured in this book is presented to take account of each general type. With lots of advice for variations you do not have to stick slavishly to the styles shown; it's better to consider your own features and adapt the style to suit. You should not feel dictated to by the pictures accompanying each hairstyle, but inspired to experiment for yourself.

There is advice on which hair colour and type are best suited to each style, and for each type and its problems there are practical tips about care and styling. Likewise, when it comes to hair colour it is essential you know which colour best suits your lifestyle. A simple way of finding your best colour is to determine your colour 'season' - are you a cool Spring, a warm Summer, a mellow Autumn or a dramatic Winter? We help you choose what is right for you. And since the best ideas are of little use if there is a lack of communication between stylist and client in the salon, there are also tips for talking to your hairdresser – regardless of type!

A classic example of a timeless hairstyle: the page boy look

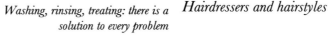

*Washing, rinsing, treating: there is a
solution to every problem*

*It can be learned: how to use curlers, curling tongs,
hairdryers and other equipment*

A new hair tone brings a new shine to hair

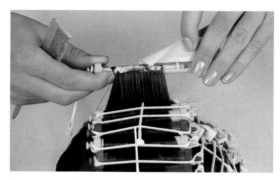

Perms: the best way to make the most of a little hair

*Cut it yourself? If you are going to do it –
then do it professionally*

CHAPTER 1

For every colour type: the right
LOOK

WHAT COLOUR TYPE AM I?

The Spring type

● Characteristics: a gentle, almost transparent complexion with a light beige undertone and peach coloured cheeks without a blue cast.

● Especially suitable: all warm tones on the blonde scale, from light wheat blonde to intensive honey blonde, or light streaks in gold blonde tones. Spring types should lighten their hair rather than darken it, to emphasise their delicate complexion.

● Avoid altogether: fiery red. If it must be red, then choose a red-blonde or a quite soft gold-orange. Also unsuitable: all dark brown tones.

The Summer type

● Characteristics: a cooler, sometimes a pale complexion. If the cheeks have colour, it will be a bluish pink.

● Especially suitable: all cool and subdued hair colours. The blonde range includes the silver tones – from platinum to ash blonde. In the case of brown colours – all shades without gold effect, and on the red scale the blue-red tones.

● Avoid altogether: dark brown tones that make the complexion look sick and pale. Also unsuitable: all copper red tones, which clearly clash with the light bluish skin colour.

The Autumn type

● Characteristics: an even ivory to yellow complexion, usually without naturally red cheeks. Often freckly.

● Especially suitable: all blonde, red and brown tones going towards gold and copper. For example, gold-orange, Titian red, chestnut and hazelnut. Even a real 'carrot top' with henna red can look great.

● Avoid altogether: proper blonde. It makes this type look pale, and blue-violet red tones make the complexion look quince-yellow. Avoid major colour changes; choose a colour that is near to the natural colour.

The Winter type

● Characteristics: either a milk white complexion without pink cheeks or an olive colour with blue tones.

● Especially suitable: all the brown tones that emphasise the dark type. Only this type can take blue-black. In the red range, suitable tones are intensive blue-violet shades such as blueberry or blackberry.

● Avoid altogether: blonde in all its variations and brown tones with copper-red highlights. They make this type look boring.

FINDING YOUR COLOUR TYPE

The colour of the seasons

The idea of colour counselling comes from America. The idea is that one particular 'season' suits each colour type and it works well - contrast the rich and cool tones of Winter with the subdued, wistful colours of Summer, the warm clarity of Spring with the shiny, earthy Autumn colours.

But which colours suit you best? This has nothing to do with when you are born or which is your favourite season. Instead it is more of a romantic classification based on your complexion colour and a colour's intensity and depth. First, if your complexion has a yellow, golden undertone you will harmonise with warm colours; if a bluish tinge then your skin will look better next to cooler colours. The characteristics of the cooler colour palette suit Summer and Winter best; Spring and Autumn types look better in warm colours.

Second, when assessing intensity and depth imagine for a moment a specific colour, say, yellow. Is it a strong, yolk yellow or a cool, lemon yellow? The creamy yellow of vanilla ice cream, a slightly red maize yellow or a gold, mustard yellow? A cool yellow will complement Summer/Winter people; a warm, gold yellow is best for Spring/Autumn types! Now we know the four colour types, how do you find out which 'type' *you* are? Remember, once you have identified your season you can use this knowledge forever - you don't usually change from one type to another!

Follow these simple rules:

1 *Remove all your make-up and wear a simple, neutral top.*

2 *Sit in front of a large mirror under good, natural light (other lights will distort your natural colouring).*

3 *Take a good, long look - what do you see? Write it down - what is your natural hair colour, your natural eye colour, eyebrow colours, complexion, cheeks, lips and eyelashes.*

4 *Then jot down the colours you prefer and which suit you best - in clothes and make-up and when your hair is coloured. What colours are you wearing when you receive the most compliments about your looks?*

5 *Now look at the basic colour characteristics for each seasonal type on the previous page and the seasonal colour ranges on the colour definition sheet. You are probably already moving towards your definition.*

6 *Remember: although some colours will suit you better than others - that is a part of your unique personality - there is a shade of every colour which you can wear. Even if you think red is not your colour there is a red that will suit you.*

7 *Compare the colours on the colour definition sheet. Try not to look at the seasonal definitions until you have made an assessment of their effect. Taking one at a time look at the four different reds against your skin and at the effect the reflected light has on your complexion. Does one make your skin look sallow? Does another highlight your pink cheeks? Which one best complements your skin and hair colouring?*

Now do the same with the other colours. If you are lucky you will find that the range of colours you have chosen all belong to one season - your very own colour season, or type. But it is not easy. If you think of the colour ranges as spreading around a

circle with each quarter representing the seasons, your unique colour 'aura' may fall anywhere around that circle.

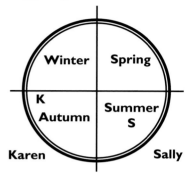

Sally (S) may find it easy to assess that she is a Summer colour type; Karen (K) may find that she is not sure about some colours.

Even within a specific colour season, some colours will suit you more than others. Think about this in terms of your wardrobe, your hair colour and your make-up. You may look best in your summer-blue using a summer-pink to highlight or accentuate.

And of course, mood and occasion are essential. Some days you can wear that really bright dress while on other days you may prefer to be more subtle.

8 *Have some fun with a group of friends and a pile of scarves or clothes - examining and comparing the effect of colours on your skin. The more you practise the more you will learn about the colours that make the very best of your looks.*

Remember: more information on this can be found in the other books in this series: *Colour You Beautiful* and *Make-up Colours and Style*.

The styling in the left hand photograph is certainly good but the hard colour contrast does not complement the naturally delicate appearance - this is achieved by the softer colours in the picture on the right

A lot lot of brown powder and rouge on a naturally more strongly toned skin (photo left) certainly looks more sporty, but also a little crude. Finer and more to type is the cooler make-up shown in the photograph on the right

Anyone with reddish hair tends towards over - or under-emphasis choosing either bland, natural colours or extreme effects such as lilac mother-of-pearl (photo left). Full, rich colours, such as those shown on the right, lend this colour type a lot more contour and definition

A woman with such intensive natural colours - dark hair and eyes, light complexion - should emphasise these contrasts. In the subdued colours on the left the effect is boring; in the photo on the right, the effect is much more exciting

CHANGING COLOUR

What is the difference between toning, dyeing and colouring, between bleaching and lightening? What creates what effect? What damages the hair and what does not?

Anyone wanting to change their hair colour must ask themselves this question: which colour type will suit me? Using the information in this chapter you will now know whether you are a Spring, Summer, Autumn or Winter colour type. Don't go against the system. For example, if you are a dark-haired Autumn, consider orange-red highlights; if you are Summer, think about ash blonde. Nevertheless, not every desired colour change can be achieved with every preparation. This applies just as much to the professional hairdresser as it does if you do it yourself. There are three basic techniques – toning, colouring and bleaching.

● In toning, pigment is lodged in the outer edges of the hairs.

● In colouring the pigment penetrates deep into the interior of the hair.

● Bleaching destroys pigment.

Left: colouring hair is really something for the professional. This is especially true with dramatic colour changes, or colours that are quite different to the roots

What hair toning can do

Whether using a mousse, liquid, cream, or a tone combined with a setting lotion, check if it really is a tone (and not just called one). The packet will indicate that the contents have no oxidisation medium that needs to be mixed in. The preparation can be applied just as it is. It is not permanent.

Typically a tone will contain 'direct drawing' pigments. This means that the colour grains are already prepared for use. They attach themselves to the hair and penetrate just a little way below the surface.

If you use a tone with a dark pigment, this will strengthen your natural colour. Pigments with the same depth of colour as your natural tone will intensify or vary the basic colour (eg with a red or silver tint).

Toning with light pigments on to a darker colour cannot be seen, but they can give a slight difference in shade to blonde or bleached hair.

Advantages of toning:

● It is very kind to the hair because it does not attack the keratin structure.

● The colour change can be reversed because the pigments can be washed out again.

● There is no problem with growing roots.

Disadvantages of toning

● This method cannot be used to lighten the hair.

● Grey hair can be given a slight shade difference, but not completely changed.

● Hair can only be darkened by two or three degrees.

On balance, toning is ideal if you want to try out a colour first.

The effect of real colours

Dyeing, or 'colouring' as most dyes are called these days, change the hair colour over a long period of time. These products can be easily recognised because the packet always contains something to be mixed in – an oxidisation medium – which is mixed with the basic colour.

The whole thing works like this: in the basic colour – usually a more or less creamy emulsion – there are a few primary constituents. These substances are made up of tiny particles. In the first phase, they penetrate the outer scaly layer of the hair. In the second phase, the oxidisation medium takes effect. It binds the primary substances of the colouring to the pigment; they are then so enlarged that they cannot leave the hair.

Advantages of colouring:

• This method permits all colour changes from light to dark.

• Lightening the hair can be done in two or three stages.

• Grey hair can be reliably covered up.

• The colour cannot be washed out.

Disadvantages of colouring:

• Depending on the intensity of the colour change, many – or sometimes a few prominent roots – will show themselves as soon as the hair begins to grow.

• If you have dyed darker and wish to return to the natural colour, it is possible, but is very stressful for the hair.

On balance, real colours are to be recommended if you want to keep that colour permanently, if lighter hair is desired, or if the grey hairs have become so numerous that they cannot easily be hidden with a tone.

What are intensive tones and soft-colouring?

Unfortunately, the instructions on toning and dyeing are not always very clear and are not user-friendly. So often 'intensive tones' and most 'tone shampoos' are in reality dyes. What makes them different from 'colouring' is the smaller concentration of the oxidisation medium.

This makes them a little gentler on the hair, but diminishes their colouring ability.

'Soft colouring' and 'acid colouring' contain just as little oxidisation medium, and are free of ammonia. This alkaline medium is harsh and is usually used to cause the scaly layer to swell, in order to make the pre-colouring stage easier.

Allergic to hair colouring?

In the statistics of cosmetic substances causing allergies, hair dyes stand near the top. This sounds more dramatic than it actually is. Those affected most frequently are hairdressers themselves, who have to handle many different chemical substances every day. Anyone who only dyes or tones their hair every few weeks is at little risk.

Despite this, anyone with a tendency to allergies should be careful. This means that someone who already has an allergy diagnosed – for example, hay fever, nickel or food allergies – should test the colour preparation first. Try it out somewhere on the body where it cannot easily be noticed, wait for 24 hours and then look to see if the skin has reddened.

BECOMING A BLONDE

Bleaching the hair should only be undertaken by those with very healthy hair, and those who are prepared to take great care of it. Only someone who is already naturally blonde should attempt to become a platinum blonde.

Different ways of becoming blonde

• Using a bleach – also called an 'intensive lightener' – is quite a process, especially if changing from dark brown to light blonde, for example. The hair has to be bleached twice, and this places enormous stress on the hair.

• 'Lightening colours' create a lightening of up to three degrees. This is sufficient to make medium-brown hair a fairly light honey blonde. Points to watch: lighteners do not always prove to be such. They are often found in the usual colourings and intensive tones of the light blonde range. Besides hydrogen, which breaks up the pigments, they also contain bleach particles, which to some extent remove the colour from the hair and colour it again with blonde shades.

• Lightening sprays can be applied to wet or dry hair. They make the hair about half a tone lighter per application.

Why bleaching on its own is usually not enough

Anyone wanting to be blonde usually has a clear idea of how they want their hair to look. However, instead of the hoped-for silvery shine, often a rather ugly yellow results. The reason for this is that every natural colour is a mixture of brown-black and red pigments, but almost always only the brown-black pigments are broken up by oxidisation; nearly all the red pigments survive the oxidisation without being affected. As a result, they determine (and ruin) the resulting blonde colour. There is a way to rectify this, by either applying a tone in the desired blonde (which will wash out), or by colouring again afterwards with an intensive blonde tone or colouring. Such procedures demand much experience and must always be undertaken by a hairdresser.

Streaks of blonde through blonde

Using a very careful highlighting technique, the hairdresser can produce beautiful lights, for example, by using a number of different blonde tones. This colour mix comes very near to a natural blonde colour.

Above: in the case of blonde tones it is important that the highlight is suitable for the complexion (ie the colour type). For tips: see pages 10 and 11

DO-IT-YOURSELF – OR NOT?

It rather depends whether you have a major change of colour in mind or only a small one, and whether the colour is to stay or be washed out afterwards.

The greatest hurdle in getting the colour you want when you are doing it yourself is choosing the correct preparation. Usually you find yourself staring at full shelves in a large chemist's shop or supermarket, with little advice available. It is therefore necessary to be well informed and prepared beforehand.

It is important to establish your basic colour correctly. This is where many mistakes are made, which means that the final colour is not what you want. The main problem: most women judge themselves to be darker than most manu-facturers' colours. As a tremendous amount of experience is needed to determine the colour exactly, here is a very useful tip: gather some hair from the comb, straighten it out and make it into bundles with sticky tape (about 100 hairs). Take these strands along with you when you go shopping and compare them with the samples on the shade card. And remember that your top hair is always a little lighter than the hair from your comb.

Left: hair colours also colour the skin and are very difficult to remove. This can be prevented by applying a greasy cream to the ears and contours of the face

Recommended: if the hair is to undergo a total change of colour, it should be left to the hairdresser.

The aim: beautiful highlights

The colour changes are minimal, but they bring a wonderful shine to the hair. And you can easily do this on your own. Look for a toning preparation without an oxidisation medium and a colour that is similar to your own: for medium blonde, choose gold-orange or a silvery ash blonde.

Important points to remember:

• The lighter your own hair, the shorter the time required to produce an effect. Otherwise you may find that instead of red highlights, a copper tone results, or ash blonde comes out too dark.

• In the case of permed or brittle hair, care must be taken. This hair is porous and so absorbs the colour more quickly.

• Dark, healthy hair needs the most time for the tone to take effect.

• Important: the highlights first become visible when you move and the light shines on to the hair. Therefore, do not try to assess the result in the bathroom mirror.

The aim: to lighten the hair

This, too, you can do yourself, as long as the hair is intact and the change you seek is not too great – for example, when you want to get a warm golden brown from a dull medium brown. To achieve this you need a colour with a lightening effect. Important: using the colour chart, decide what lightening is possible from what original colour. The first time you try this procedure allow less rather than more time (but never less than stated on the packet), so the hair does not turn out lighter than desired.

Another possibility is to have lighter strands that do not necessarily have to be blonde. A gentle red in chestnut brown hair makes the overall tone lighter and livelier. Combed highlights, too, are relatively easy to achieve. The highlighting preparation – a lightening cream – is combed into the covering hair with a wide-toothed comb.

Another way of appearing blonder is to just lighten the hair a little around the face. This can be done with a lightening spray. But be careful. Do not use the spray more than two or three times on the same spot. The reduction of pigments using this method is difficult to control; too frequent use can mean that over time the blonde hair can become too light.

What should always be left to the hairdresser:

• Clever highlighting with different colours.

• Lightening of (dark) coloured hair.

• Making permed hair blonde.

• Lightening darker roots. Here, quite accurate work is required, otherwise the result will be much lighter than intended.

• Major changes of colour from dark to light. Only a hairdresser can judge how much the hair structure will stand.

1

3

1 *If two substances have to be mixed together before using a toning preparation, it will be an oxidisation hair colour. This means that the colour is permanent and cannot be washed out.*

2 *Mousse toners can usually be washed out afterwards; they are used as they are on the hair.*

3 *Tips for applying toning preparations. Begin at the neck, the hair is usually healthy here and therefore takes a little longer than the porous hair on top to absorb the colour. Hair ends that have lost their colour should be treated last of all. They absorb colour very quickly and easily become too dark or too red.*

4 *Plastic gloves prevent fingers and fingernails taking on the colour.*

5 *Toning preparations usually do not drip. However, a plastic cape or a piece of aluminium foil will protect clothing, walls or furniture, if the hair should touch it. Important: the times recommended on the packet should be strictly adhered to. Mousse toners have an intensive effect if they are left in the hair too long. In the case of oxidisation toners, the colouring process may sometimes not be completely finished if they are washed out too soon. This is especially true of blonde colours. Use a kitchen timer!*

The aim: a great red

Starting with a basic blonde to light brown, it is very easy to get a really good red by toning. If you have a darker hair colour, you nearly always need a dye or at least a strong tone, otherwise only red highlights will result. With red in particular, the intensity of the tone can be controlled very well by the time allowed for it to take effect. It is preferable to keep the time short if the original colour is blonde and the hair a little worn. If you are not careful, the tone can become too strong. If you do not want to take any risk, only leave the toner on for a few minutes – for the minimum recommended time. It can always be strengthened later.

Red effects that are best left to the hairdresser:

● Fashionable red tones that have to be precisely applied to get the correct tone. The experts in the salon simply have more experience.

● Difficult red shadows that have to be put in the hair using different techniques. They look much smarter than an even red.

The aim: to become darker

Nothing could be simpler, and it is much kinder to the hair than lightening because no pigments are destroyed, but others are added. There is only one stress on the hair when darkening it – the opening of the scaly layer to facilitate the first step in colouring. With gentle colouring, it is a fairly kind process, as are tones that just stick to the surface. However, anyone wanting to dye their hair black should be at least medium brown to begin with. For those whose hair is any lighter the change is too great; you will need proper dye (ie colour). A rule of thumb: darkening two to three steps more is always best.

What the hairdresser can always do better:

● Dye or tone darker, long, permed hair and hair damaged by the sun. Because its structure is never even and the porous places absorb the colour much more easily, this can lead to mottled results if you try it yourself. The professional prevents this by evening out treatment beforehand and by careful application.

● If the hair was previously coloured blonde or highlighted, there is also the danger that the colour will be uneven. Here, also, it is best to turn to an expert.

NATURAL COLOURS

Natural organic colours are the trend these days, reflecting increased environmental concerns and health awareness. However, not all the colours you may want can be found in the range of these colours.

Organic colours are now found in conventional hairdressing salons, and are no longer considered 'alternative'. A whole series will be found in the range of almost every large manufacturer of hair cosmetics. Hairdressers are taught how to use the powders and granules, as colours using plant pigments demand sensitive use.

Plant colours are true tones

This means the pigments only attach themselves to the surface layer of the hair, without penetrating where natural and artificial pigments are seated. In these surface layers, however, the natural colours attach themselves much more firmly than usual toners, which means they last longer. This is especially true of red tones. Despite this, there is little problem with natural colours when the hair starts to grow again at the roots, since no great change in colour is possible and the colours are more translucent in their effect.

What is and is not possible with plant colours?

Natural pigments give the hair particularly soft and flattering shades (very similar to plant textile colours), especially with warm brown, gold and red tones.

• Brilliant colours or great colour changes are not possible. The great appeal of plant colours is that they create shades of the natural hair colour.

• Lightening is not possible with plant colours. For this a chemical oxidisation medium is required.

• Neither can they be used to cover up grey hair. However, lightly greying hair and even white hair can be given shades and interesting lights.

The greatest advantage of plant colours

• The effect is produced not just by the plant pigments, but also by other constituents, for example, astringent substances that make the scaly layer smoother and more stable. Every treatment with plant colours protects the hair at the same time. The result: glossy hair.

• Plant colours do little damage to the environment, either in manufacture or use.

Changing from normal to plant colours

• Anyone who has dyed their hair for many years using normal colours (not tones) may find a problem. It is not always possible to treat dyed hair with natural colours.

• It is easiest if you just slightly lighten your own colour or change the tone a little. A professional hairdresser will be able to achieve the change of colour – even if it is necessary to have a number of treatments.

• If the hair has been strongly lightened, plant colours can bring a different shade to the hair but they will always darken it a little. The red tones are tricky, because they inevitably turn out stronger in worn ends.

• It is rather difficult with dark coloured hair when the roots have to be matched. The solution lies in a careful combining of plant and chemical until the 'artificial' colours have grown out.

What you can do for yourself

Anyone with healthy hair that is untouched by chemical treatment can experiment with plant colours without problems. The powders are obtainable in health shops in many different colours – and recently in supermarkets.

The right amounts should be mixed with hot water, according to the instructions, to make a paste, and then applied evenly to wet hair. The time required for it to take effect differs according to the colour, from half an hour to an hour.

During this time, the colour paste should be kept warm and moist – only then can the pigments penetrate. It is a good idea to cover the hair in foil, and wrap a warm hand towel around the head, with a second one on hand.

Advantages of plant shampoos and tea rinses

Rinses with camomile tea have been in use since our great-grandmothers' time. They are supposed to make blonde hair even lighter. Unfortunately, this is not what happens: the yellow pigments of camomile are stored in the hair and give it a light gold effect.

Shampoos with plant colours have a stronger effect – but not immediately. Shampoos containing camomile, with continued use, produce a golden tone; shampoos with henna give a pretty red tone; and walnut shampoos gradually intensify all brown tones.

Natural colours produce particularly soft tones. Blonde hair acquires beautiful golden highlights with camomile, cinnamon, hops and turmeric; for dark hair, use ivy sandalwood, walnut, and madder roots. Henna is ideal for red tones

For every length:
TIMELESS STYLES

- Hair analysis

- 12 super styles for short hair

- 10 styles for medium-length hair

- 9 styles for long hair

- How do I tell the hairdresser what I want?

Discover your hair type, which hairstyles suit you, your colouring and your lifestyle and where to find relevant tips for hair care in this book.

In principle one head of hair is much like another, whether it grows thick or thin, straight or wavy from the scalp. It is made up, like the hard layer of outer skin or fingernails, of dead cells – so-called keratin. However, hair keratin has an especially ingenious structure. As a result hair, in contrast to nails, is hard yet elastic, firm yet malleable. If you look at a cross-section of a hair under the microscope, you will see groups of fibres wrapped around an airy centre, and joined together with a sticky substance. They are also covered with a thick scale layer to protect the inner hair.

Heads of hair also vary considerably in quality and condition. These differences are important in deciding which style is suitable for you.

In addition, remember your colouring and lifestyle. If you lead a business life, you may prefer to keep it short, neat and with easy-to-maintain colour; if you have more time or your work depends on looking good, a longer style with a major colour change may be more appropriate.

For these reasons, the following short descriptions of the more common types of hair also contain advice on suitable styles and tips on hair care.

Normal, healthy hair

● *What does it look like?*
Normal, healthy hair is elastic, can be styled well and combed when wet without problems. It is springy, shiny and malleable, because the scale layer makes the surface smooth and closed.

● *Which styles are suitable?*
In principle, everything is possible, since the hair is not especially thick or thin. It can be permed without too much difficulty.

● *How should you take care of it?*
You do not need to watch anything in particular; see tips for washing and care on pages 65-71.

Fine, thin hair

● *What does it look like?*
It lacks strength and fullness, due as much to the lack of hair volume as to the narrow diameter of each hair. As the hair has a lack of elastic fibres, it is both loose and soft. One advantage, however, is that as a result the hair is more easily shaped. The disadvantage is that it loses its shape much more readily.

● *Which styles are suitable?*
All are possible, but especially those styles which emphasise fluffiness and volume – for example those on pages 30, 33, 34, 37, 40 and 44.

HAIR ANALYSIS

● *How should you take care of it?*
With treatments, described on page 73.

Greasy hair
● *What does it look like?*
It is straggly, sticky and damp, the hair sticks to the scalp, and the shape loses its volume and lightness very quickly. This is due to an over-production of scalp grease, which is also particularly runny and so spreads quickly over the head.

● *Which styles are suitable?*
All uncomplicated styles which do not need lavish styling, so that the hair can be washed daily, or at least every other day. See examples on pages 29, 31, 33, 37 and 39.

● *How should you take care of it?*
Use special products which have the same effect as blotting paper, and slow down the spread of grease through the hair.

Dry, unmanageable hair

● *What does it look like?*
It is often dark or red. The individual hair has particularly strong kertain fibres, which usually resist all attempts at styling. It also has a mind of its own and tries to grow in its own natural direction. The hair flies about easily, and loses its shine, because too little scalp grease is produced.

● *Which styles are suitable?*
Styles that take account of the crown and fall of the hair, so that the hair retains a good shape without styling (see page 38).

● *How should you take care of it?*
With products that contain

substances that supply grease and shine to the hair. A little 'ballast' of this kind allows obstinate hair to look well kept and makes it more amenable to styling. More about this under 'brittle hair', from page 77.

Porous hair

● *What does it look like?*
The surface of the hair is roughened, the scale layer is coming apart and is therefore porous. In the case of longer hair the lower third is usually affected, because the hair is not cut as often as short hair and therefore deteriorates over time.

● *Which styles are suitable?*
The hair should be cut – in serious cases in stages – until the porous hair ends have disappeared, because porous hair retains no shape and always appears a little untidy.

● *How should you take care of it?*
If the whole hair is affected (because of too much exposure to the sun or an unsuccessful chemical treatment), special preparations used after every wash can help to restore shine and malleability (at least on the surface). More about this on page 77.

Naturally curly hair

● *What does it look like?*
From strong waves to fine curls, it is nearly always robust and strong, but often dry to strawy.

● *Which styles are suitable?*
All curly styles that do not need drying or putting in rollers, but that can dry on their own. Examples on pages 31, 32, 39, 41, 47, 49, 50, and 52.

● *How should you take care of naturally curly hair?*
In principle as you would for dry, stubborn and/or porous hair, so that the hair becomes softer, shinier and more malleable. More from page 80.

Hair with a crown

● *What does it look like?*
Superficially, the hair appears to fall straight, but in certain places it grows in crowns, defying all styling attempts.

● *Which styles are suitable?*
Those that take the crown into account, so that they look 'intentional'. Another possibility is a perm so that the crowns disappear.

● *How can you take care of it?*
With treatments that suit the hair type.

Permanent waves

● *What do they look like?*
Depending upon style and type, they can be wavy or curly. The condition of the hair is usually dry, especially at the ends, to porous.

● *Which styles are suitable?*
Curly styles that can dry naturally, but also those with curls and waves that are simply dried with a hairdryer or rolled up to retain the style for a time.

● *How should you care for your perm?*
With special treatment for permed hair, or, if required, with treatment for dry or brittle hair. More on page 119.

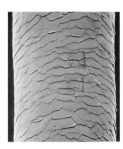

Left: a hair with damaged scale layer
Right: an intact hair

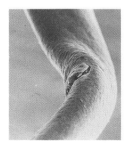

Left: a broken hair with frayed fibres
Right: a hair damaged by elastic bands

STYLES FOR SHORT HAIR

Forehead wave

● *Who does this suit?*
Women who like to look sporty or dress elegantly. It's particularly pretty for natural, grey or ash-blonde hair with highlights on top.

● *Which hair type is ideal?*
The stronger the hair, the better. This style favours a light natural wave because the hairline is more easily retained.

● *Points to remember about this style:*
From the parting both sides fall evenly to the centre of the ears, at the neck/chin angle. (See photo below). From there it is gently layered. It's a style that lies close to the head, and makes a particularly pretty head shape.

● *Styling:*
Apply spray setting lotion to the hair and dry it over a thick, round brush. Shake it towards the back and apply hair wax to the ends. Push the wave into the face.

Brush cut

● *Who does this suit?*
Uncomplicated or sporty women who do not want to be bothered with a lot of styling. Especially good for natural, uncoloured hair.

● *Which hair type is ideal?*
This cut is suitable for every type of hair. It is, however, important to have a good hairline at the neck and, as the style lies very close to the head, a face which is not too large, and pretty ears.

● *How is the hair cut?*
The hair is layered and cut blunt at the neck and sides. Cutting evenly, by moving the scissors from side to side whilst cutting, thins the hair too much. The back of the head and fringe are emphasised. The hairdresser will therefore use a special technique: using the scissors, he or she will cut vertically into the hair. In this way the style can be shaped exactly.

● *Styling:*
Rub a blob of styling mousse the size of a pea on to the palm and rub it into the fringe. Then slide both hands through the hair against the direction of growth.

Bobbed hair

● *Who does this suit?*
All young, sporty women, who dress fashionably. Deep, rich colours are good for bobbed hair – chestnuts, auburns, the darker shades.

● *Which hair type is ideal?*
Fine to strong hair that can be made very straight. It is also suitable for natural waves which can be blow-dried straight.

● *Points to remember about this style:*
The hair should be absolutely level across the base of the ear lobes, and cut blunt. It requires great accuracy so only the best hairdresser is good enough.

Important: have a trim every four weeks, otherwise the edges will look ragged.

● *Styling:*
After washing, apply mousse. Roll up the hair on large rollers from the parting and leave to dry, or blow-dry over a thick, rounded brush. Backcomb lightly from underneath at the roots.

Finally, use some hairspray on fine hair to give it some body.

Cropped hair

● *Who does this suit?*
Young women with a feminine aura. It can work well with sporty clothes. It particularly suits women with fine facial features, small ears and a pretty hairline. Good for Spring and Summer colours – light, fair and blonde, even a good grey.

● *Which hair type is ideal?*
Strong hair with light natural curls, because then the hair ends look best. Straight hair is also suitable, but it must be helped along with hair gel or wax. Be careful with thin hair; the scalp shows through and makes it look even thinner.

● *How is the hair cut?*
The hair at the neck and sides is cut literally to a millimetre length; on top of the head the hair is somewhat longer. The fringe will measure about four centimetres.

Important: frequent trimming is needed, so the tousled fringe retains its lift.

● *Styling:*
Simply wipe styling cream or hair wax across the flat of the hands and work through the hair. Last of all twist the fringe at the front with the fingertips.

Curly mop of hair

- *Who does this suit?*

The sporty as well as the elegant. If you have a round face you need to be careful, in this instance the hair should be a little longer at the sides.

Avoid solid colours with this style: too ageing. The curls lend themselves too experimentation with coloured layers – blondes, browns and reds. Great for grey hair.

- *Which hair type is ideal?*

Normal to strong hair, with natural curls for best results, but also fine hair with a light perm. It should not be too thin.

- *Points to remember about this style:*

The hair needs a lot of volume, for this reason the top hair is lightly layered, and from the neck to level with the earhole it is cut well away. This leaves the back of the head looking really pretty. The side and top edges should be lightly feathered, so that the transition from the curly top to the layered contours appears particularly soft.

- *Styling:*

Work styling mousse into all of the hair and just leave to dry. Then spread styling cream on to the palms and shape using the fingertips. Gently stroke the side hair narrowly back.

Hedgehog cut

- *Who does this suit?*

Young women with narrow faces, good skin and a pretty neck. Looks especially smart with feminine dresses and skirts.Good for daring multi - colour schemes but only for the youthful!

- *Which hair type is ideal?*

Very straight hair, then the 'spikes' stick out very well. Styling preparations also produce the same effect.

- *Points to remember about this style:*

The sides should be quite narrow, and fall for the full length of the neck. The hair is bluntly layered all round at about one centimetre, with about two centimetres on top.

- *Styling:*

Put some mousse in the hand and apply to the hair. Let normal and strong hair dry naturally; fine hair should be dried with a dryer against the fall of the hair. The fringe can be made to stand up (pictured left) by using gel and a comb.

Layered bob

● *Who does this suit?*
Sporty, natural women, who just run their fingers through their hair and, despite chin-length hair, want to look smart whatever the weather.

● *Which hair type is ideal?*
Fine to strong hair. A long neck helps. This style hides forehead crowns and ears that stick out, and flatters a strong jaw line.

● *Points to remember about this style:*
The top hair is blunt cut becoming shorter towards the outside. To achieve this when cutting, the hair must be pulled away a section at a time. The reason for using this technique is to make the hair appear fuller. At the neck the hair is finely layered and chin length (photo below).

● *Styling:*
Apply styling mousse to the hair and blow-dry over a round brush. Blow the roots against the direction of growth and fix with some hair spray.

Mushroom cut

● *Who does this style suit?*
Sporty, natural women of all ages. Tip: cuts with shorter fringes always make you look a little younger. Darker shades outline the shape well; if lighter colours are preferred, consider light highlights (or lowlights).

● *Which hair type is ideal?*
Strong, but also fine hair. Even thin hair seems to have more volume with a mushroom cut .

● *Points to remember about this style:*
The long, ragged fringe falls from the crown at the top of the head, a trick that makes the whole style look fuller. The sides are layered to above the top of the ears, and the side-boards only lightly thinned, making it look quite full. The length on the top of the head should be about seven centimetres. At the neck the hair is cut quite thinly and lightly feathered.

● *Styling:*
Blow-dry the hair on the top of the head on a round brush until dry, then shake into shape. In the case of fine hair apply a small amount of mousse beforehand to give it fullness. Pull the hair ends into strands with gel.

Doll style

● *Who does this suit?*
Young, fashionable women, who sometimes like to wear sixties make-up. This asymmetric shape is especially attractive for chubby cheeks and distracts from skin imperfections.

● *Which hair type is ideal?*
It looks at its best with full, dark hair with light, natural waves. The shinier the hair, the better it looks. Great care is needed.

● *Points to remember about this style:*
The hair falls from a deep side parting to as far as the ear lobe (photo below); on the longer side it falls as far as the chin, and has lots of volume. At the ends it's lightly layered, the fringe cut at an angle, and the hair closely cut at the neck.

● *Styling:*
Whilst blow-drying the hair, brush it with a skeleton brush from the back to the front and vice versa. Then shake the hair into shape and set with a little hairspray.

Feather cut

● *Who does this suit?*
Delicate featured women with a nicely shaped head, pretty ears and a long hairline at the neck. The more feminine the woman, the better the feather cut will look.

● *Which type of hair is ideal?*
Fine hair with light, natural curls on top. In the case of very straight hair, a light perm in the section above the forehead is a good idea.

● *Points to remember about this style:*
The hair is even all round, but layered quite short, and is only four centimetres longer above the forehead. The neck section should also be thinned, so that it tapers out nicely with ragged ends.

● *Styling:*
Apply mousse to the hair and using the fingers tousle into shape. Last of all, lift the fringe around the brush and blow dry.

Garçon cut

● *Who does this suit?*
Tomboys, natural women. As the hair can fall where it wishes, this style is suitable for all those who find styling a problem. The cut is particularly attractive for ash blonde or light brown hair with golden or copper-coloured streaks.

● *Which type of hair is ideal?*
Thick, full hair, straight or lightly waved.

● *Points to remember about this style:*
From the crown to the upper edge of the ear, the hair is cut bluntly all round. The neck section is layered and has a light bow shape. So that the shape remains round, do not remove too much hair from the back. The side and forehead sections are lightly layered into each other.

● *Styling:*
Apply mousse and finger comb to all sides while blow-drying. Finally, tousle the sides forwards with a little gel. Dry the damp fringe from beneath with the hairdryer.

Fuzzy curls

● *Who does this suit?*
All romantic women, who like practical hairstyles. Suits those with small heads, natural make-up and strong red lips. It is an ideal cut for those whose hair becomes greasy quickly, because the wet-look hides this.

● *Which hair type is ideal?*
Naturally wavy, or permanent wave. The hair should be fine, but not too thin. Fuzzy curls are especially pretty in dark and in bushy brown hair.

● *Points to remember about this style:*
The hair is bluntly layered all round to a length of four centimetres. The sides and the fringe are a shade longer and cut slightly feathered. In this way they lie close together and curl very well.

● *Styling:*
Dry the hair with a hand towel and then knead mousse into the hair. Leave to dry on its own. To achieve the wet look take another couple of small blobs of hairstyling cream, rub between the hands and knead well into the hair.

STYLES FOR MEDIUM-LENGTH HAIR

Short bob

● *Who does this suit?*
All young, elegant women, who need to look smart, particularly at work.

Important: this does not suit those with a short neck or high a forehead.

● *Which hair type is ideal?*
Fine to normal hair, if possible straight. This is a cut that particularly brings out the best in very blonde and very dark hair.

● *Points to remember about this style:*
In contrast to the equal lengths on each side, the hair on the top of the head at the back is cut just a little shorter and layered so that it falls round. The neck section is short and well cut. Important: regular trimming is essential.

● *Styling:*
Apply hair mousse and blow dry the hair over a large round brush. Brush into shape, apply a little spray and then comb over the top hair.

Fuzzy waves

● *Who does this suit?*
Fuzzy waves not only suit every type of woman – old or young – but also almost every type of fashion. All colours are suitable – good for lighter, summer tones and lowlit darker shades. Great for well conditioned grey hair.

● *Which type of hair is ideal?*
Fine, naturally wavy or strong hair, which has been treated with a light perm.

● *Points to remember about this style:*
When straight, the hair is the same length all round. It falls loosely from the parting on both sides. On the longer side, the front strands are layered so that the hair falls loosely into the face. Regular trimming is important so that the curls retain their shape.

● *Styling:*
Dry the hair with a towel and apply styling mousse. Shake the hair forwards, work through and dry using a diffuser – most hairdriers can accommodate one, or you can you buy them as a separate attachment. It's a special fitting, which diffuses the air gently without blowing.

Chin length flicks

● *Who does this suit?*
Individual women who prefer a style that, despite or even because of its timelessness, suits every fashion.

● *Which type of hair is ideal?*
Fine, preferably dense hair, best of all blonde. Also great: brunettes with golden highlights. In all cases, a small face is best, with a small nose and dark eyebrows.

● *Points to remember about this style:*
From the side parting, the hair is cut straight to chin length in different sections. To do this, the hairdresser holds the individual strands a little way from the head. By using this technique the covering hair is made a shade shorter, which optically provides more volume. To create the fringe over the forehead, divide a centimetre of hair over the forehead and cut into strands.

● *Styling:*
Roll the hair over a small round brush outwards and blow-dry. Comb upwards and spray hair lacquer into the ends from below. Comb the fringe flat against the forehead and allow to dry on its own.

Inward curl

● *Who does this suit?*
All girlish-looking women with a larger face. (Women with small faces do not look their best with such a volume of hair.) Most suited are those with a high forehead and a short neck.

● *Which type of hair is ideal?*
Strong, healthy hair in a beautiful brown. Anyone who finds their hair colour somewhat uninteresting can tone it with hazel or gold.

● *Points to remember about this style:*
The hair is cut a section at a time level with the chin, with the top hair a little shorter than the hair underneath. In this way, the inward roll holds better. For the fringe, one-and-a-half centimetres of hair is divided over the forehead and cut into strands at eyebrow level.

● *Styling:*
Simply blow-dry everything inwards over a large brush. Finally, brush well against the direction of growth, throw the hair back and shake into shape.

Round style

- *Who does this suit?*
All lively blondes, who would like the top cut, but are not looking for a formal style. Very suitable for round faces, a strong neck and not quite perfect ears.

- *Which type of hair is ideal?*
Fine hair, also thin, with streaks, which gives a more voluminous appearance. A variation would be with gold blonde highlights, that become light flaxen at the ends.

- *Points to remember about this style:*
The parting is very high. The straight edges fall all around in a light arch. At the back, the hair is chin length; at the front it reaches up to the tip of the nose (photo below).

- *Styling:*
Work in styling mousse and whilst blow-drying keep pulling the hair forward with a medium-sized hairbrush. Then spray the hair from underneath.

Page-boy cut

- *Who does this suit?*
As the page-boy look is so varied, it is a classic style which suits most women and looks especially nice with sporty clothing. Page-boys are best in darker shades – mid-browns to blue blacks – as these best define the shape. Glossy conditioning is essential.

- *Which type of hair is ideal?*
Fine to strong hair, that grows absolutely straight. In the case of wavy hair, it is always necessary to keep blow-drying it, as the page-boy style always looks best when absolutely straight.

- *Points to remember about this style:*
Whether at chin or shoulder length, the classic page-boy style is cut level in sections. The neck section is always cut a little shorter. This optical illusion is important, so that the hair will look all the same length when the head is held level. The fringe falls level with the eyebrows and must be absolutely straight from temple to temple.

- *Styling:*
Apply mousse, and using a skeleton brush draw the hair away from the head in all directions while blow-drying.

Strand cut

● *Who does this suit?*
Sporty, but also feminine types. As the hair – when cut correctly – always keeps its shape, this is a style that suits everyone who is in a hurry.

● *Which type of hair is ideal?*
Normal to strong hair. The cut looks smarter with dark hair (and light skin) than with blondes.

● *Points to remember about this style:*
The back and front are the same length, but the side ends – as with a short fringe – are cut in strands. So that it looks quite pointed, the hairdresser will accentuate the edges again at the end. When trimming, the scissors are held vertically in the hair ends, so the shape can be more easily achieved.

● *Styling:*
First apply styling mousse to the damp hair, then pulling the hair into the face, blow-dry strand by strand using a skeleton brush. If a quick job is required, ruffle the hair forwards with the fingers when blow-drying.

Layered waves

● *Who does this suit?*
Small, even-featured faces. Anyone preferring to have their hair off their face altogether must wear make-up, otherwise the overall effect will be too plain.

● *Which kind of hair is ideal?*
Strong hair, with natural curls or a perm. The style is more effective on dark hair than on light.

● *Points to remember about this style:*
So that the fullness remains in the neck, the collar-length hair is only lightly layered. The sides are cut diagonally starting from the temples, so that the waves from the side parting fall away nicely towards the back.

● *Styling:*
Rub firm-hold mousse into the wet hair and comb everything towards the back with a broad-toothed comb. Allow to dry on its own. Put some hair wax on the fingers and spread over the surface of the hair with the palms.

Curly bob

● *Who does this suit?*
Young women who like to dress a little elegantly. Pretty for small faces with high foreheads.

● *Which hair type is ideal?*
Strong hair with a light perm or natural waves. As these sort of curls are held with styling mousse and can therefore look dull, it is recommended that the hair is frequently toned with mousse.

● *Points to remember about this style:*
The whole style is combed from the back to the front and cut round and level in front of the face. At the sides it is cut to chin level, and the top reaches to the tip of the nose. Shaken into shape, it is lightly tapered. The neck section is then finally cut straight.

● *Styling:*
Apply some styling mousse over the whole head; hold the head under the diffuser and finger dry. If the hair is not very curly it can be wound around styling rods.

Classical bob

● *Who does this suit?*
Young women who like a classical look but also want to look modern. The style looks good on someone with a low forehead, larger face and big cheeks. This bob is suitable for all coloured hair; dark shades hold the shape well but lighter, highlighted browns and blondes can look stunning.

● *Which type of hair is ideal?*
Fine to normal hair. If the shine has gone, treatment is necessary from time to time. Highlights should be very fine, and should be freshened up every two months or so.

● *Points to remember about this style:*
The ends are level all round and cut absolutely straight. It is essential to have a first-class hairdresser who can cut the sections precisely. So that the ends do not look ragged, it will need a trim every four weeks or so

● *Styling:*
Add styling mousse to the hair and use a large round brush to pull individual strands outwards from the head whilst blow-drying. Then there will be no old-fashioned inner roll, but still plenty of volume to the hair.

STYLES FOR LONG HAIR

Lion's mane

● *Who does this suit?*

Young girls and young women with especially good hair quality and good skin. It is a distinct advantage to have a face that is not too small, a pretty hairline and small ears. Stunning on richly lit blonde or deep auburn, chestnut or black. Condition must always be the very best.

● *Which hair type is ideal?*

Healthy, strong hair with natural waves. Then the waves on the forehead will stay in place. It's also suitable for hair with a good perm. To avoid having hair with a rather tired appearance, however, it is necessary to follow up with a half-perm every two to three months.

● *Points to remember about this style:*

The hair is longer than shoulder length, cut straight to one length, and slightly rounded. As such long hair has a tendency towards split ends, it will need to be trimmed every six weeks or so. It is important that the hair shines, so give it frequent special treatments and a good rinse after every wash. An ice-cold finish rinse adds shine.

● *Styling:*

Spray all over the head with styling lotion and leave the hair to dry on its own. Spread a little hair wax on the fingers and stroke backwards into the hairline.

Hollywood waves

● *Who does this suit?*

Only very young girls with pretty hair and even features. The style is ideal for the evening, especially with Hollywood-style outfits.

● *Which hair type is ideal?*

Thick, healthy hair which is brown, blonde or red. High lights do not look right in this style. However, anyone wanting to lighten their hair can separate a few fine strands to right and left of the parting and lighten these. This looks as if it has been lightened in the sun.

● *Points to remember about this style:*

The hair is cut straight and level with the shoulder blades and lightly rounded, that is, in sections. The hair on the top is cut a little longer to give the inner roll more support. It is very important to have a trim every six weeks.

● *Styling:*

Dry the hair in very large rollers. Then brush well with a skeleton brush in all directions, make a side parting and style the inner roll. Apply a little hairspray to the front.

Angel's hair

● *Who does this suit?*
Feminine and romantic young women, also sporty types who like to dress like a tomboy.

● *Which hair type is ideal?*
Natural waves, and not too fine hair with a permanent wave. Wind hair in styling rods, then the curls come out best.

● *Points to remember about this style:*
Starting from a high parting, all the hair is cut level and straight. The forehead section and the sides are slightly layered, so that the hair has a fuller or blown appearance.

● *Styling:*
Spray setting lotion into the hair and blow-dry; continue to add more spray while doing this, and afterwards use your fingers to arrange the hair carefully. Pretty variation: pin the hair up loosely all round (photo below).

Shoulder length hair

● *Who does this suit?*
All those who like a sporty look and value a good style but do not wish to bother with a great deal of styling.Good for mid, dark and highlighted paler shades; not good for greying hair.

● *Which type of hair is ideal?*
Thick, healthy hair with a beautiful shine. A coloured highlight rinse from the hairdresser will help achieve this.

● *Points to remember about this style:*
The hair falls level all round from the side parting. The fringe is cut in centimetre widths on the forehead, and then into strands using thinning scissors. Important: the sides are somewhat 'sharpened', to make them springy. To do this the hairdresser takes a few individual strands, places the open scissors diagonally in the lower third, and pulls the scissors slowly through to the ends.

● *Styling:*
Take normal setting lotion and blow-dry the hair whilst combing with a skeleton brush away from the head. Finally, brush the ends outward.

Layered curls

● *Who does this suit?*
Women of all ages who like a classical look. It is important that the face is open, that the woman has good skin, a forehead that is not too round, and discreet make-up.

● *Which type of hair is ideal?*
Full, thick, strong hair that is easily put into rollers is best. Layered curls look especially pretty in brown tones.

● *Points to remember about this style:*
The hairdresser will comb the whole hair from the back to the front and then cut it level in front of the face. He or she begins this level with the mouth and cuts diagonally downwards on both sides, until the scissors touch the shoulders on the sides. Shake the hair back to produce pretty curls.

● *Styling:*
Apply styling mousse and lightly remove excess water with a blow-dry. Then put the hair into middle-sized rollers from front to back and finish drying. Brush the hair forwards over the whole head, then shake the head backwards. Finally fix with some hairspray.

Blonde mane

● *Who does this suit?*
Only very young women with good skin and a preference for classical fashion and pin-up hairstyles. As long, straight hair of this kind does not keep its shape the day after washing, it needs some skillful care.

● *Which type of hair is ideal?*
Normal to fine and thick hair. The style looks best with really straight hair and a shine – but requires a lot of attention. Try careful use of straighteners.

● *Points to remember about this style:*
The hair falls away from the parting in one length and is just lightly rounded at the sides. As unevenness is immediately visible, it will be need to be trimmed by about a centimetre every four weeks to keep it level.

● *Styling:*
If possible, let the hair dry by itself; after that blow-dry all over for a short time. This produces greater fullness.

Grace Kelly waves

● *Who does this suit?*
All women who prefer a very feminine style. If the hair is plaited (photo below), this style goes well with jeans and leather jacket.

● *Which type of hair is ideal?*
Fine to strong, straight hair, natural blonde. Natural red, or with highlights.

● *Points to remember about this style:*
All the hair is cut level to shoulder length. The hair underneath, however, is a little shorter than the hair on top.

● *Styling:*
Apply styling mousse, and pre-dry the hair lightly. From the side parting, from top to bottom, roll in medium-sized rollers and finish drying. Then brush the hair out on all sides, comb into shape, and push a wave towards the face. Apply a little hairspray.

Square cut

● *Who does this suit?*
Young women who like the tomboy-look, but also want to look sexy. It particularly suits long, narrow faces with a high forehead and small nose. Good for all Autumn colours – particularly dark.

● *Which hair type is ideal?*
Normal to strong straight hair. The squared cut looks best if it is washed daily.

● *Points to remember about this style:*
The hairdresser will cut this style a section at a time, carefully pulling it away from the head with the hand to achieve minimal layering. The top hair is cut just a little shorter at the ends so the style looks fuller. A fringe is cut, coming from the crown. Despite the fullness, it should not be too heavy, and is therefore thinned at the edges.

● *Styling:*
It is best to leave the hair to dry on its own first and only finish off with a blow-dry.

Banana

This is the greatest of all classical styles for long hair: timeless, elegant and modest, yet modern and very sexy.

Anyone choosing this style will need at least shoulder-length hair. Strong hair can be pinned up straight away; fine hair must first be rolled briefly using electric curlers, so it stays together better and is easier to shape.

1 *First comb the hair through and then backcomb. To do this the comb is moved up and down behind every strand close to the head.*

2 *Now divide the hair level with the ears right across the head, hold the top half tightly and carefully brush the surface straight.*

3 *Put the brush aside. Twist the upper section to the right into a thick cord.*

4 *Then pin the cord into a roll.*

5 *Now take the lower part up and brush straight from underneath.*

6 *Then twist into another cord to the left. If you have done it correctly, it will nestle closely to the head on its own.*

7 *Hold everything in place with pins. Finally, secure the ends of the lower roll into the upper roll.*

Do you always have problems at the hairdressers?

This does not need to happen if you express your

wishes clearly, and take note of any objections.

HAIRDRESSERS/ STYLES

Short hair? Let's see ...

Ideally the hairdresser and client should make a perfect team: the hairdresser makes fashion suggestions, but considers the client's preference. The client allows herself to be persuaded if professional advice goes against her ideas. Unfortunately, this ideal situation is all too rare. Usually the customer does not express herself clearly enough, and the hairdresser does not take sufficient account of her wishes.

Thus frustration for both is inevitable. Communication can, however, be vastly improved – by giving the hairdresser a chance, and by not changing to another every time you are disappointed with your haircut.

How do I find the best salon?

The best thing to do is to try to find a good hairdresser through friends and colleagues, by asking them where they have their hair done. It should always be remembered, however, that many salons portray a particular image that suits their own style. For example, some very 'trendy' hairdressers are known for their up-to-the-minute styles, not for classical waves and precision cutting. Hairdressers who have a reputation for cutting are not the best to go to for long styles, and the nice little salon round the corner is unlikely to be the place to go for outlandish colours, as they will have too little practice or experience.

First of all, it is essential to make an appointment for a consultation.

Good hairdressers will always be pleased to find time for a consultation without obligation or cost to you. On this occasion, you should not just look at the hair of the customers present, but also at the hairdresser's. Their appearance is usually a good indication of the direction and taste of the salon. During the consultation it will also become clear how interested they are in fulfilling your wishes.

• Go to your consultation or first appointment dressed in a way that expresses your usual style.

• Do not let the hairdresser cover you with an overall; they need to see all of you, not just your head.

• Apply your make-up with as much care as you would normally (even though you must expect it to get spoiled as the hairdresser works).

• Go with freshly washed and styled hair. This also gives the hairdresser an opportunity to get to know what type of person you are and your tastes. This will have a great bearing on the hairstyle you will have.

You must speak to your hairdresser, without fail, on the following points:

• First and foremost discuss the new style you want. It is good idea to look through a folder of styles together with the hairdresser. First let him or her suggest what they think suits you. Then explain what you had in mind. The advantage of this is that you will get ideas you would not otherwise have had.

How would it look with a fringe?

Just trim the ends, no problem!

● Even if you do not want a completely new hairstyle, if possible clarify all the details exactly, because if they are not exactly right, they can be the cause of great disappointment – for example, a parting that is in the wrong place, a fringe that is too short, or hair that is a crucial centimetre too short over the ear lobe.

● If you are changing your hairstyle, you should be sure to make it absolutely clear how much time you can spare each day for styling. You must be quite honest and not deceive yourself. If the style is really pretty but needs a lot of attention, in the long term it will not bring much pleasure.

● A good hairdresser must establish what chemical treatment your hair has already undergone, and speak to you about this.

● If you want to have a perm, you must explain exactly how straight, wavy or curly the hair is to be. This is the most frequent cause of displeasure; either the waves are too strong or too weak. This can be due to a mistake by the hairdresser, but more often it is due to a misunderstanding between hairdresser and client.

What if things go really wrong?

This can happen, either because you have not explained your wishes carefully enough, or when there has been a real mishap. Do not just swallow your anger in such circumstances, but complain. It is best to wait until the initial anger has subsided, then return to the salon and argue your case quietly and objectively. It is best to speak to the proprietor right away. A good hairdresser will have a sympathetic ear for complaints. After all, he or she earns their living by satisfying their clients, and will often suggest a free correction of the problem, if the question of fault is clearly resolved.

A correction means that the hairdresser attempts to put the fault right. This is not always so easy, but there is nearly always something that can be done. A wrong colour can be put right later; a permanent wave can be strengthened or weakened. If the hair has been cut too short, it is difficult to glue the ends back on again, but the hairdresser can at least offer to wash and re-style it until it has grown back again.

It is almost always possible to come to some agreement.

To make sure that in future no such mishaps occur, it is always a good idea to ask yourself if you are not a little to blame as well. Mistakes occur most frequently when a hairdresser tries to satisfy a client's wishes, which on professional grounds should be refused.

High forehead? Already gone

CHAPTER 3

For every type of hair: everything that keeps the

HAIR
healthy

- The right shampoo

- Care and protection

- Creating volume

- Avoiding a greasy shine

- Getting rid of split ends

- Letting it grow

- Controlling curls

- Stopping hair falling out

- Doing away with dandruff

- Avoid the sun

THE RIGHT SHAMPOO

Washing the hair is the first step to beautiful, shiny, full hair.

Your choice of shampoo plays an important part in this.

People think that washing hair is such a simple thing that you cannot do anything wrong. But you certainly can!

Here are eight rules for washing your hair to give it maximum protection:

• Before washing, brush thoroughly. This loosens the little pieces of dirt and the remains of styling products.

• Pre-rinse the hair with lukewarm water. This helps to save on shampoo.

• Use only a little shampoo; in the case of short hair, a blob the size of a hazelnut is sufficient.

• Do not apply the shampoo directly to the head. First rub it into the palms and then spread evenly over the hair with open fingers.

• Do not rub the hair, just work the shampoo in gently.

• Do not leave the shampoo in the hair for too long. It only takes a few seconds for the washing and conditioning agents to work.

Left: does frequent washing harm the hair? This depends not only on the shampoo used, but also on how the subsequent drying and styling is done

• It is very important that after washing you rinse the hair thoroughly, as shampoo residues can reduce its shine and volume.

• Finally, gently squeeze out water from the wet hair with the tips of the fingers, lightly dry with a towel, and wrap in a hand towel – just as you would when washing fine woollens. When drying the hair with a towel, avoid rubbing.

Wet hair should be handled with 'velvet gloves'

In its dry state, a natural hair fibre is amazingly robust and even harder than a fingernail. This changes at once when the hair becomes wet. The outer scaly layer swells in water and becomes extremely sensitive. If the hair is combed or brushed carelessly, individual scales can be split or pulled out altogether. This inevitably reduces resistance, shine and malleability.

Therefore, when combing or disentangling wet hair a wide-toothed comb should be used. Be careful to check that the comb has no rough edges or corners that can tear open the scaly layer. The use of a brush of any kind when the hair is wet is absolutely taboo.

Also important: when untangling hair, always begin with the ends and gradually work upwards. This saves unnecessary pulling and tearing. If the hair cannot be combed out without tugging and pulling, this is a sure sign that the hair is already damaged.

Washing daily – does it harm the hair?

If the hair is intact, it can be washed every day. Modern shampoos are so mild that normal, healthy hair should be able to withstand daily shampooing with no harm coming to it. This is also true for greasy hair. Research has shown that the scalp does not get greasy more quickly as a result of frequent washing, assuming that the preparations used do not cause drying out.

With long hair, or hair that has been put under strain, you should think carefully before deciding if it really is essential to wash the hair daily. This is also true of a dry scalp that is occasionally taut or itchy.

1 *Shampoos that sting the eyes are relics of the past. Modern products protect skin, hair and eyes.*

2 *A lot of foam does not necessarily mean the shampoo is more effective. Shampoos can be made in such a way that they do not produce foam at all and clean thoroughly despite this — these are particularly protective. The fact that foam producers are included in shampoos has more to do with psychology than necessity - people feel the cleaning process is going on and feel they have more control rinsing out the shampoo.*

3 *Thorough rinsing is important if the hair is to shine and look full. Medium to long hair should be rinsed for at least three minutes. A cold spray at the end is good for the circulation of the scalp and aids shine.*

4 *Before combing, soak up the wet from the hair with a fluffy towel. Do not rub, but twist the towel like a turban and leave on the head for a few minutes.*

5 *A shampoo or 'hair bath' marked 'mild' is absolutely recommended. Tip: when buying, take care that the contents are not too runny and the bottle opening not too large, as this makes it difficult to use the shampoo sparingly.*

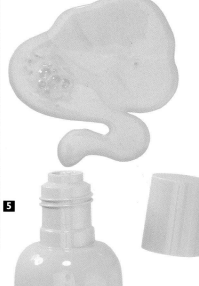

Every wash – even with the mildest shampoo – will to some extent cause stress to the hair and scalp, as will combing wet hair. Avoid both of these on a daily basis if you have sensitive hair.

The right shampoo

There is a shampoo to suit each hair type and wash it perfectly. Not every product is suitable for every type of hair or every hair problem.

● *Shampoos for normal hair.*
These preparations can do one thing: clean. And if they are good, they do it in a very gentle and protective way. Normal hair does not require more than this.

● *Shampoos for fine hair.*
These are sometimes called 'volume shampoos' and contain, besides very mild washing agents, substances that make the hair a little stronger and fuller (eg keratin, silk protein, or herb extracts). These substances help the hair to keep its shape, and bring more airiness and fullness to the style.

● *Shampoos for greasy hair.*
These, too, contain first and foremost a mild, cleansing agent, most importantly to protect the scalp. Substances such as conditioners and those that add grease are left out, however, as they would overburden the hair and make it heavy. Active substances include anti-bacterial and slightly roughening herb extracts. These are intended to

normalise the production of grease on the scalp, so that after washing the hair does not quickly collapse and look lank.

● *Shampoos for dry and damaged hair.*
These preparations contain oily substances to improve condition, such as lanolin or lecithin, as well as synthetic sticky substances, that make the hair more malleable and straight. They can close the tiny splits in the scaly layer of the hair and can make wet hair easier to comb. In the case of fine hair, a build-up of grease or dry ends, these 'conditioning shampoos' should not be used. The conditioning substances can overburden the hair, so that it collapses quickly. In this case it is better to use shampoos especially for greasy hair, with occasional treatment for the ends (see also pages 74–75).

● *Two-in-one shampoos.*
This is the name for those shampoos which contain a conditioner as well. These are a good idea when you are in a hurry and do not have the time to spend on extra treatment. Just washing the hair gives it more shine and makes it easier to comb. However, continual use of these products can lead to problems. For example, the addition of silicone can, with time, lead to a build-up on the surface of the hair; these layers will make the hair lifeless and heavy. If this happens, the hair should be washed for a time with normal shampoo, until the remains of the silicone are removed.

● *Strong cleansing shampoos.*
These powerful cleansing shampoos remove a build-up of conditioners in one go (see above). This can be necessary, and makes sense if you have a permanent wave or a new colour in mind. A build-up of silicone can have a negative influence on the chemical processes involved in this treatment.

● *Anti-dandruff shampoos.*
These contain washing agents that loosen tiny pieces of skin from the scalp especially well, and also prevent further build-up of dandruff (more of this on page 89). In addition, good hairdressers wash with special shampoos selected after careful analysis of the hair. The preparations can, as a rule, also be obtained for use at home. Tell the hairdresser only to wash your hair once if you washed it the previous day.

WHAT CAN HAIR TREATMENTS ACHIEVE?

Brittle ends, lack of shine and no vigour in the hair? This all points to holes in the scaly layer. Treatments can repair them.

Conditioners, treatments and repair products can certainly make hair more beautiful – immediately and more permanently – because they improve the resilience of the hair and to some extent actually repair damaged hair. This 'mending' of the hair is not completely permanent, but works at least from one hair wash to the next.

However, too much or the wrong treatment can also do damage when, for example, the hair has been made limp and unmanageable by treatments. Products and the frequency of their use must be carefully matched with hair type.

How much treatment does the hair need?

A small test will help you to find out what care your hair needs and can tolerate. Put a cross alongside the points that apply to your hair, and follow the care tips in the text where you have made the most crosses. If there are the same number of crosses in two different groups, this demonstrates that the hair is more worn out at the ends than in its upper third.

After application, spread the cream treatment with a large toothed comb. Take great care with the ends of the hair.

'Light' treatment

- The hair structure is fine.
- The hair quickly becomes greasy.
- The hair cut is fairly short.
- The hair is not dyed, nor has it a permanent wave.
- After washing it is easy to comb.

With hair in this condition, it is usually sufficient to give it a light rinse without grease enhancers. Quick liquid treatments that can stay in the hair are also good.

'Medium' treatment

- The hair is chin to shoulder length.
- The top hair is a little bleached by the sun.
- The ends are a little brittle.
- When combing wet hair, it pulls a little.
- The hair is dyed or streaked.

Hair in this condition can do with a rinse that repairs the tiny splits, and from time to time also needs a treatment for the porous ends.

'Intensive' treatment

- The hair is longer than shoulder length.
- The hair has a perm.
- It lacks shine and malleability.
- The hair is highlighted more than four shades from its natural colour.
- After washing, it is quite tangled and very difficult to comb.

This hair can take conditioners with oil additives, and needs regular intensive treatment.

Conditioners: what they can do and how to use them

Conditioners or 'balsams', are not as intensive as a hair treatment. Their task is, after washing, to straighten the lightly roughened, scaly outer layer of the hair so that it is easier to comb. As a more even surface reflects the light more strongly than a rough one, the hair has a deeper shine after using a conditioner.

Conditioners are used after washing. They are best applied to hair dried with a hand towel. Apply the preparation sparingly and evenly, and wash it out after one or two minutes. It is not necessary to leave it on for any longer.

Is it necessary to use a conditioning treatment after every wash?

This all depends on the hair and the product. In the case of normal conditioners, the hair-smoothing effects will be retained until the next wash. However, there are products containing a strong glueing substance, such as silicone and polymers. They are largely contained in conditioners for badly damaged and porous hair, and can last for several washes. When using these, however, you must take care to find out how much is good for the hair. If, after a time, it becomes heavy and lifeless, it is best to wash the hair without using a conditioner for a few times.

Quick treatment for more springiness

These liquid treatments in bottles or sprays contain especially light conditioners and moisture providers. As these quick treatments contain little or no grease, they are best for fine hair and hair which becomes greasy easily. Spray treatments are more suitable when the top hair is somewhat rough and dry but the hair underneath is completely intact. These are practical because quick treatments do not need to be rinsed out, but remain in the hair. As many products also contain a consolidating agent, styling aids such as gel or a styling mousse can be dispensed with.

When do you need a thorough treatment?

Treatments comprising a cream or oil should basically only be used on damaged hair. They are intended to repair cracks and holes in the scaly layer of the hair and provide the hair with oils and moisture agents to make it softer, more malleable, and easier to style. This becomes necessary if the hair has had too many perms or bleach treatments, or if you have been sitting unprotected in the sun for too long, or have been in chlorinated or salt water for too long without rinsing the hair properly afterwards (see further page 91). Rough, physical treatment can also damage the hair so much that it loses shine and elasticity, for example, by too much back-combing or the continual use of unsuitable combs and brushes (see also page 79). Hair treatments can, to some extent, repair damage, not permanently, but for a certain time. With good preparations, substances that have built up in the hair will survive three to four washes.

How treatments work best

Hair treatments as a rule contain similar substances to those found in conditioners but in a much higher concentration. However, they need a longer time to be absorbed by the hair (approximately 15 to 20 minutes). This process can be intensified by warmth. After application, a piece of aluminium foil can be wrapped around the head and a pre-warmed hand towel tied around it. It is important that the treatment is thoroughly rinsed out.

Conditioning treatments are among the products offered by hairdressing salons. They will have preparations which are even more suitable for specific hair problems than those available for home use. You should not skimp on conditioning your hair particularly after a colour rinse or perm.

Professionals apply treatments strand by strand and work the preparation in lightly with the fingers. In this way all the hair is reached and not just that on top, which can easily happen when it is applied in one go and spread over the head by hand.

1 *Why does the hair shine particularly after a hair treatment? Because the surface of the hair has been smoothed and reflects the light better.*

2 *Hair treatments need a few minutes to work to be really effective. During this time the hair should not become cool. Wrapping a pre-warmed towel around the head is recommended.*

3 *Split end treatments give even very damaged ends a more cared-for appearance.*

4 *Do-it-yourself treatments with kitchen ingredients are too fiddly to use and are inferior to most of the commercial products available. However, if you want to have a go anyway, try this: mix an egg yolk with a few drops of lemon, apply to freshly washed hair, dry with a towel, and leave to work for half an hour. Finally, rinse out very thoroughly, so that the hair does not smell musty.*

5 *The ends of long hair can be specially treated with a cream when they are twisted together.*

6 *Split end treatments glue the hair ends temporarily, but are no substitute for regular trimming of the ends.*

FINE HAIR

There is nothing that can make a lot of hair out of a little.

However, there are a few tricks in care, cutting and styling that

increase the volume.

There is nothing that can be done about the diameter of fine hair, which can often be half that of thick hair. What you can do these days, however, is improve the hair structure with cosmetic remedies. Use substances (eg calcium binders) that not only attach themselves externally, but also penetrate into the surface of the hair. For a time they make the hair firmer and more manageable. Keratin, collagen and silk proteins also make the hair stronger. Another way of making fine, soft hair more manageable is to use conditioners and treatments that leave a gentle film on the hair and 'separate' the hairs a little from each other.

What is most important is the correct cut

● Fine hair, whenever possible, should not be allowed to grow beyond shoulder length. This is because the length must always be in a sensible proportion to the volume if the hair is to look healthy and the style good.

Left: fine hair immediately looks fuller if the ends are cut level

Right: for more volume, special shampoos are available

● Hair cut level rather than layered is always better, as sparse hair collapses quickly.

● On the other hand, some hair cut shorter than the rest is an advantage as it provides support where required, for example, at the back of the head.

Styling tips for fine hair

● Move the parting about a centimetre every so often. In this way, you will prevent the hair from always going flat at the parting. From time to time, move the parting to the other side of the head.

● Styling mousse and hair spray are the best styling aids, because they give the hair more shape and body. Wax and gel are best avoided on fine hair; they make the hair too heavy and remove volume from the style.

● After washing, finish the half-dry hair with a blow dry. This gives lift at the roots.

● The hair will have great shape and volume if all the hair is brushed forwards towards the face when dry and then lightly sprayed on top. This will also lend shape and body to the hair underneath. Then throw the hair back and finish styling.

● Back-combing fine hair can give the appearance of volume. It is usually sufficient to lift the roots a little using a back comb.

Tricks with a perm and colour

On the whole permanent waves are a good way of giving the hair an appearance of having volume. However, in the case of fine hair, this presents the hairdresser with a real challenge. Thanks to new preparations and rolling techniques, a perm for fine hair is no longer the problem it once was, and the hair itself is not damaged. To be particularly recommended are the alkaline-free 'acid' wave preparations.

GREASY HAIR

A problem that stems from the scalp. Unfortunately, this problem cannot be cured, though no one needs to go around with grease-streaked hair.

There are two main causes of a fast build-up of grease in the hair: either the sebum glands produce too much grease, or the amount of hair is insufficient to take up the normal quantity of grease produced. In the case of fine hair, there is often a third factor as well – perspiration from the head. This, too, can create strands of greasy hair.

How to care for greasy hair

The production of sebum cannot be controlled from the outside, since it is fixed genetically and controlled by hormones. However, a lot can be done to deal with the grease itself.

For example:

● Hair that becomes greasy quickly should be washed as often as necessary. It has been shown that frequent washing does not in itself encourage the production of grease.

Left: treatment sachets can be used to treat greasy hair and prevent the formation of greasy strands

Right: a similar effect can be gained by using shampoos for greasy hair

● Care products designed for greasy hair should be used, as they will most certainly not contain grease, wax or other substances that make the hair heavy and cause it to collapse more quickly.

● When washing and drying, lukewarm temperatures are preferable. There is no evidence to suggest that grease production is encouraged by high temperatures; however, the grease itself becomes runny with high temperatures and thus spreads more quickly throughout the whole hair.

● Do not comb greasy hair too often. Likewise intensive brushing can also spread the grease unnecessarily over the whole head.

● Washing the brush and comb when washing the hair, is very important or the grease will be put back into the hair when styling.

The best styling tips

● It is best to choose an uncomplicated style, then daily washing is not a real problem.

● Avoid styles that lie close to the head, or the hair will quickly absorb grease.

● Gentle back-combing holds the hair off the scalp and hinders quick greasing-over.

● Hairspray and setting lotions are a good idea for greasy hair, because they separate the individual hairs.

● If the hair is very greasy, perms and streaking can be a help. Both make the hair a little more porous, so that the grease is absorbed by the hair.

● If you do not have time for a complete wash, just wash the fringe and re-style. This gives the whole style a better appearance.

● Other possibilities: use a wet-gel to create a 'wet style'. Then it does not look so obvious if the hair is not quite morning fresh. Greasy hair can also just be a temporary phenomenon. This happens especially during periods of stress. When the stress is over, the sebum production returns to normal. The contraceptive pill can also be a factor in the rapid production of hair grease.

BRITTLE HAIR

Whether the hair is naturally dry or has become rough through treatment, it is possible to restore its shine and malleability.

When hair grows from the scalp it is normally quite healthy. The scale layer is closed and the hairs are shiny and malleable. Unfortunately, this situation does not remain as hair grows old. As hair grows fairly slowly – about one to one-and-a-half centimetres per month – by the time it reaches the ear lobes it will have been growing for about a year. With only two cleansing and styling procedures per week, it will then have had over a hundred washes, about 24 hours blow-drying and several thousand brushing and combing strokes. Some damage is inevitable. The scales that protect the hair are used up a little at a time, and the hair loses shine and tangles easily. As this process continues, eventually the inner fibres will be exposed. This is clearest at the ends – where they split. Things do not need to go that far, however.

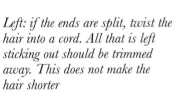

Left: if the ends are split, twist the hair into a cord. All that is left sticking out should be trimmed away. This does not make the hair shorter

Brittle hair needs careful handling

Hair that feels rough is highly sensitive; it no longer shines, and is difficult to style because of cracks and holes in the scales. It is essential to handle it very carefully, especially when washing. It is best to use a conditioning shampoo, which contains grease agents and 'repair substances', which do not roughen the hair any more but smooth it. It is quite important that after every wash, you use a conditioner (especially for damaged hair) so that the comb goes through the hair more easily and the scaly

1 *Preparations to treat split ends contain silicone, which glues the cracks and covers the ends with a protective film.*

2 *Damaged, brittle hair should not be brushed, otherwise it becomes even more roughened. However, hair that is dry by nature likes being brushed because in doing so the grease from the scalp is distributed as a natural softener over the whole head.*

3 *To untangle the hair: after washing use a wide-toothed comb with a smooth surface, which does not damage the scaly layer. Undo knots with great care; never tear or pull.*

layer is protected. After every third or fourth wash, instead of a rinse use a proper cream treatment. This contains a higher concentration of 'repair substances' and is therefore effective for much longer.

How 'repair substances' work

Many preparations for brittle, split hair bears the technical term 'active polymer'. This indicates that the product is a synthetic composition of giant molecules containing a positive charge of electricity. Their effect is as follows. When the hair has been damaged, the chemical characteristics of the keratin, of which the hair is composed, change. Because of these changes the damaged parts draw care substances towards themselves like a magnet. The holes in the scaly layer are filled as a result and the hair becomes manageable and shiny again.

Silk proteins, collagens and keratin bindings are closely bound to the hair. Panthenol is also helpful, a derivative acid from the vitamin B complex, it provides more moisture and elasticity. Fine oils such as wheatgerm or jojoba oil provide a gentle film that protects and makes hair more malleable.

What you should not do to damaged hair

● Back-combing. This roughens the damaged surface even more. If you have to do it, use a comb and only back-comb a little at the (healthy) roots.

● Do not use electric rollers or curlers every day. The dry heat draws the moisture out of the hair and makes it even more brittle.

● Avoid permanent waves and intensive dyes, and trim particularly damaged ends.

● Lengthy periods of sunbathing should be avoided. Use a UV shield for the hair or – better still – bind the hair in a scarf (see also page 91).

What is really helpful for split ends

Thanks to new products, split ends can now be treated quite well cosmetically. Silicone bindings glue the split ends together and coat them in a protective film. This temporary repair will withstand a few hair washes, but must be renewed. The application of a few drops of split end treatment should be rubbed between the fingers and applied to the ends of the hair, strand by strand. If the hair is already too badly damaged, there is only one remedy – cut the ends.

Split ends can be prevented by what is known as 'split cutting'. The very ends of the hair are cut regularly. This prevents the broken ends from splitting and tearing further up the hair.

Problem: dry scalp and brittle hair

This is not due to daily wear and tear; the sluggishness of the sebum glands is the cause of the problem. They produce too little grease to make the hair manageable. The problem here – as with greasy hair – is genetic.

Basically the care required is the same as for dry hair. In addition, massages to the scalp are recommended to encourage blood circulation, best of all with a hair lotion containing a stimulating herb extract and gentle oils. To massage, place the fingertips on the scalp and gently move the fingers in a circular motion, or push the skin together. Also good: the famed one hundred brush strokes a day. These stimulate the scalp and spread the grease available evenly throughout the hair.

1 *Combs with wide teeth are best for wet hair and for combing through natural or permed thick curls.*

2 *Combs with a handle enable strands to be divided cleanly.*

3 *The different lengths of the teeth in this comb makes back-combing particularly easy. With the fork at the end it is possible to lift up the hair in sections, in order to give the hair that extra refinement.*

4 *Hand-cut horn combs are expensive, but very kind to hair. The outlay is worthwhile.*

5 *Metal combs look attractive, but often have sharp points. Before purchasing, test the teeth by touching them.*

6 *Natural bristles give the hair a particularly good shine. Especially suitable for straight, long and dry hair.*

7 *Brushes with rounded plastic bristles protect the hair, they are easy to clean and very good for untangling and styling. The skeleton brush (above right) has a good grip and helps add lift at the roots when blow-drying; the half-round shape brings volume to the hair; the round shape assists the creation of curls.*

LONG HAIR

The problem here is the ends. In caring for the hair it is important to keep it healthy and to avoid split ends by gentle handling.

Because of its age, long hair will also have a lot of treatment behind it. This shows itself particularly in the lower third of the hair. The structural difference between healthy roots and worn ends is often tremendous, and when caring for your hair attention must be paid to this. Products made especially for long hair are recommended; they keep it smooth and straight without being harsh. Select a shampoo and conditioner especially made for this type of hair, and use hair treatments only on damaged ends.

Very important: do not allow the hair to grow unchecked, but have the ends trimmed regularly. Then there is not much chance of the ends splitting. It is also a good idea with long hair to have it cut into shape, because it looks better kept. Somewhat shorter support hair underneath also makes sure that the length has the volume it needs.

Left: if freshly washed hair is flyaway, there is a very simple trick to get rid of the electrical charge – cream the hands lightly and softly stroke the hair

Good for long hair

• Damaged ends should be washed with just a little hair treatment. This protects them and prevents an unnecessarily long wash.

• Apply shampoo, diluted with water, from a squeezy bottle, to the roots of already dampened hair. When rinsing, all the washing agent will then be spread throughout the whole hair and still clean it sufficiently.

• Whenever possible, let the hair dry on its own.

• Very important: do not tie the hair too tightly, and use covered elastic bands or scrunchies.

1 *With long hair it is particularly important to trim the ends about every four weeks. It then not only looks well cared for, but also fuller.*

2 *Because of its age, long hair needs a more frequent cream treatment than short hair.*

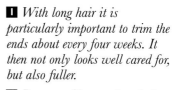

3 *Preparations specially made for long hair contain substances that keep the hair healthy, but do not make it heavy.*

NATURAL CURLS

These can be very obstinate to deal with, but they can be tamed with cutting and care. Then they are nearly always a dream!

Naturally curly hair possesses in abundance the springiness that is missing in straight hair. On one hand this is something positive, because curly hair looks very vigorous and natural, but it is difficult to shape because it always springs back into its natural position. The best way to deal with this is to use a treatment that makes the hair somewhat heavier. Suitable preparations can be found in product ranges made for dry and brittle hair.

Put a real shine on magnificent curly hair

Natural curls look particularly beautiful when they have a high gloss. This is often missing, however, not necessarily because of hair damage but because of the characteristics of curly hair. The structure of its keratin is naturally a little more brittle, and above all the wavy surface does not reflect the light as well as straight hair.

More shine can be achieved on curly hair by using a special 'shine spray' containing oils, or

The curls form more attractive ringlets if you dampen them. Rather than water, use a gloss or special spray to 'restructure' or refresh the hair; this is better than water, and also takes care of the hair

a spot of burdock root oil. Pour a little between the palms and spread on the surface of the hair.

How to make curly hair easier to style

• A good style that takes into account the natural direction in which the hair grows is vital. Attempts to work against nature with curly hair are bound to fail.

• Layered cuts are best. They make the hair easier to style. A further advantage is the curls look more generous and beautiful.

• Partings and fringes always create problems for curly hair. If possible avoid them. Real professionals cut curly hair twice: a rough cut while it is still wet, and then a fine cut when dry. The reason is that curly hair always looks longer wet than dry.

• Ideal styling aids are styling creams and hair wax. They give more gloss to the hair, which is usually dull, and give the curls a particularly good structure.

Artificially straighten natural curls? Better not!

All procedures that attempt to straighten curly hair are, in the long term, stressful for the hair, and seldom achieve the desired effect.

Permanent wave preparations can be used to straighten curly hair if it is rolled onto appropriate large curlers. Despite this, however, after every wash the hair must be straightened with a hairdryer and brush. This will adversely affect the hair structure and it will not look so natural.

Another possibility: comb dry the hair in wide flat sections combed around the head and hold it with long clips. Place a large roller at the crown.

HAIR LOSS

When does hair loss become an illness? What are the causes?

How can one stop hair loss? What can men do about baldness?

Each hair has a limited life. When this is reached the hair falls out to make room for a new one. Active growth lasts from three to seven years – in exceptional cases a little longer. Then the hair root stops its metabolic activity. The hair loosens itself within two to four months and finally falls out. Up to 100 hairs a day can be lost in this way; from an average of 100,000 hairs on a head, this does not present a particular problem.

Alarming signs: hair on pillows and cushions

Anyone who thinks they are losing more hair than is normal should count very carefully what is lost over a period of three days, including those hairs that end up in the comb, the wash basin or on their clothes.

Important: do not wash the hair during these three days and only begin to count the day after washing. You should also check each hair to see if there is a little white knot at the end of the hair (the root). If this is

Left: massage stimulates the blood circulation in the scalp and so strengthens the roots. Place fingertips firmly on the scalp and massage in circles.

missing, then it is generally only a case of broken hair; this should not be included in the count.

If you find a lot of hair on the pillow in the morning, it is a cause for concern. An accurate examination is now recommended.

Hormones can be the cause of hair falling out

The influence of hormones is the most common cause of hair loss. With men this can lead to baldness; in women to diffuse hair loss. Diffuse means that the hair does not fall out in one spot but over the whole head. This hair loss is usually less noticeable in women than men, and is also easier to treat, if the hormone imbalance does not correct itself.

Where hormones are a factor

● Hair loss after pregnancy, when the oestrogen balance suddenly sinks. During pregnancy a high amount of oestrogen provides for a longer growth period of hair. This is suddenly interrupted after birth, so shortly afterwards large amounts of hair can drop out. This is not a cause for concern, however. Hair growth adjusts and returns to normal after the hormone situation gets back to normal. After six to eight months, the former quantities of hair return.

● Occasionally the pill can lead to hair loss, especially when its oestrogen quantity is relatively high. In cases of particular sensitivity this hormone can have a similar effect to that of the hormone testosterone, which causes baldness in men. This is not a cause for anxiety, however, as it does not have the same disastrous effect in women as it does in men. Besides you can change to a pill with a weaker dose. If there is not only greater hair loss, but also greasier facial skin and scalp, then you should consult your doctor.

● Hormone disturbances which lead to hair loss are comparatively rare, and when this does happen hair loss is usually only one of many symptoms. As soon as the hormone disturbance has been treated, hair growth problems remedy themselves.

What influence does diet have on hair growth?

Quite a lot. This is because everything that the hair needs for growth is taken from food. Despite this, however, there is not a particular diet or particular nutrients that especially encourage hair growth. A varied and adequate diet is all that is required. This is something to remember – especially when trying to slim. A diet which is not varied and balanced, and in particular lacks protein and iron, can lead to hair loss.

It will stop as soon as the diet is properly balanced again.

Sickness and stress can disturb hair growth

Diffuse hair loss can arise in certain circumstances, for example:

● Stress. Everyday stress can weaken hair growth, but rarely leads to real hair loss. However, unusual stress, for example, examinations, emotional problems, or sickness can provoke genuine hair loss. Typically, hair drops out after a delayed period of time, from two to three months. The cause is thought to be a temporary imbalance of hormones.

● Sickness – especially feverish infections (for example, severe pneumonia) – can be followed by hair loss.

●Some medicines (for example, preparations that prevent blood clotting) under certain circumstances reduce hair growth. Fortunately, in all these cases the hair grows again as soon as the problem is over.

When should the doctor be consulted?

If hair falls out in clumps, or if the hair loss continues for a long period without any recognisable cause, it is wise to consult a doctor. Even better: have a hair consultation at the nearest skin clinic. Here you will be certain to see a specialist.

A trichogram is usually carried out, in which the amount of hair loss and its general condition is examined. From the results, the doctor can establish where to look for the cause and whether the condition needs treatment. It is usually possible to prescribe a specific form of treatment.

Hair loss or hair breaking off?

If the hair decreases in fullness, this does not necessarily mean that the cause is serious hair loss. Hair breaks and hair loss often look very similar. In the case of hair breaking, there is also more hair in the comb and on the pillow. In contrast to hair loss, however, the hair roots are nearly always completely healthy. Only the hair itself has been put under stress; being unable to take any more physical damage, it breaks off – sometimes very close to the scalp. The cause is usually a bad perm, bleaching which is too strong, or both.

A further possible cause: a fungal attack of the scalp as a result of untreated dandruff. This infection can affect the scalp and its roots so much that only weak, breakable hair is produced.

Whether hair 'just' breaks or falls out can be established by a good hairdresser. The solution to the problem: a short haircut as an immediate measure, and in the case of dandruff, an intensive scalp treatment (see also page 88 and following.)

Do hair growth products really help?

Cosmetic hair lotion and treatments are so-called 'unspecific' treatment methods. This means they work more or less on the 'watering can method'. Clearly, an effective therapy is only possible when the cause can be established. Even a doctor cannot always decide what this is. Nor can the success of hair-growth products be guaranteed; some really help, others not at all.

As a rule, such products contain circulatory and metabolic tissue extracts, herb extracts and protein ingredients. They are intended to encourage the roots to produce healthy hair and supply them with the necessary substances. There is a prospect of success when these powerful treatments contain relevant substances that by chance are missing in the hair roots.

On balance, give it a try. It is not likely to do any real harm.

What can vitamin pills and gelatine capsules do?

Every hair root requires many different vitamins and minerals (trace and mass elements) to function properly. Whether additional amounts of these substances have any effect depends solely on whether any of those substances were missing in the first place. This is difficult to identify in individual cases, and would require a lot of research. Vitamin and gelatine preparations can be useful, as can silica and calcium ampoules, if you have had an unbalanced diet over a long period of time (for example, when slimming), and there is some kind of deficiency.

Why it is difficult to help bald men

As previously stated, the cause of baldness in men is hormonal – there is an over sensitivity of the hair roots to the male sex hormone testosterone. In time its influence wears out some hair roots to such an extent that they are only able to produce a thin downy hair (no bald head is completely bald). This process can begin quite early, occasionally a few years after puberty. First signs are thinning of the temple hair, beginning to show a receding forehead. When and in what state the baldness stops cannot be predicted. Not all hair roots on the same head are affected in the same way by the hormones. Many men remain only half bald for the rest of their lives.

The possibility of stopping or preventing hair loss has always been remote. Cosmetic and pharmaceutical preparations which are supposed to encourage the growth of hair roots have had a few individual signs of effectiveness. However, a generally effective remedy has not been found. This would only be possible if the influence of the hormones on the hair receptors of the roots could be blocked. This has not yet been achieved.

DANDRUFF

A disorder of the scalp, which can and should be treated. Dandruff can lead to hair loss.

The cells of the scalp continually renew themselves. They move to the surface and are gradually pushed off. This happens daily and often without being noticed.

These dead cells first become visible as dandruff, when many become stuck together. A single white piece of dandruff consists of between 500 to 1000 hardened cells. The reason for the sticking together is the hardening of the scalp skin, the cause of which is still uncertain. As the production of dandruff is accompanied by an increase in sebum secretion, experts believe that the bacterial decomposition of the grease produces substances that provoke excessive hardening.

From time to time, however, dandruff can appear when the scalp is very dry and irritated, caused by poor shampoos, chemical treatments that are too strong, or because of excessively hot dry air. Such dry dandruff usually disappears on its own, as soon as the irritation of the scalp has disappeared.

Left: before washing the hair, brush the scalp and hair thoroughly. Dandruff is loosened and is easier to wash out

The best way to get rid of dandruff

Even the most stubborn greasy dandruff does not need to be a permanent problem. Modern substances make it possible to normalise the scalp in a fairly short time. They loosen the dandruff present and prevent excessive hardening.

Anti-dandruff shampoos contain the lowest content of anti-dandruff ingredients, but the treatment is often sufficient. In stubborn cases, additional use of special treatments is recommended. Almost all these products are applied to the scalp before washing. The hair is divided into sections and the product spread over the whole scalp and left for a while to work. In really serious cases, soothing and softening scalp treatments by a hairdresser help to solve the problem.

Repeat the process as required

After at least three weeks, the head may appear to be free of dandruff – but unfortunately not permanently. The tendency remains, since treatment only deals with the symptoms. The dandruff can return. When it does, new treatment is needed, and this should be undertaken without delay. A scalp full of dandruff makes a very good breeding ground for bacteria and yeast fungi. This could lead to the added problem of the disruption of hair growth leading to hair loss.

Washing the hair often, and keeping brushes and combs clean is important.

When dandruff becomes a case for the doctor

Psoriasis is a dandruff disease. Its symptoms are like normal dandruff, but:

• The dandruff shows stubborn resistance to all cosmetic treatments, or only improves a little.

• The skin along the hair line is not just full of dandruff, but also reddened.

In these cases, you should consult your doctor.

SUN PROTECTION

Hair too is threatened by UV light. The hairs bleach and become brittle. Protection from the sun has become even more important for the hair.

Not only the skin but also the hair can be badly damaged by ultra-violet light. The reason: under the influence of UV light, water develops similar characteristics to hydrogen peroxide, the old, well-known hair bleach. Pigments are destroyed; as a result, the hair colour becomes lighter and weaker, and the structure more porous. For this process to begin, the hair does not necessarily need to be wet – normal air and scalp moisture is already sufficient.

The sun also removes the moisture stored in the keratin in the hair, making it strawy and less elastic.

The more closed the scaly layer, the less exposed to possible damage by UV light. Special attention must therefore be given to permed, coloured and bleached hair, as well as long and brittle hair.

Left: nothing shows off shiny hair better than sunshine However, it needs protection from ultra-violet light to remain beautiful

What hair needs on a holiday in the sun

• A preparation with UV filters (spray, wet-gel, or cream).

• An especially mild shampoo with moisture binders and grease replacers.

• Hair treatments and conditioners that add moisture, and in the case of long hair, an anti-splitting fluid.

• A sun hat or headscarf to protect the hair, especially at midday.

• And one more tip: have any permanent wave done a week before going away on holiday.

1 *On the beach a cleverly tied headscarf and large sun hat are the best protection against the sun – particularly recommended for dyed or permed hair.*

2 *After swimming, rinse the hair with fresh water, because salt and chlorine residues in the hair will damage it (especially when combined with sunlight).*

3 *Hair gel containing a UV filter helps to counter the detrimental effect of sunlight on hair colour and quality – especially important when swimming.*

CHAPTER 4

For every style:
PERFECT STYLING

- Blow-drying:
  the best tips

- Curling tongs:
  how to use them

- Rolling up hair
  the right way

- Making waves

- Giving hair body:
  professional styling tips

PERFECT BLOW-DRYING

Blow-drying is more than simply drying the hair. Anyone using a brush and blow-drying correctly will add more volume and shine to their hair than if they left it to dry naturally.

Important tips for blow-drying:

• Medium-length and long hair should first be blow-dried all over. Let the hair hang over the face and when drying brush from back to front against the direction of growth. When the hair is half dry lift the head and blow-dry the hair into shape.

• With short hair, first blow-dry it into shape, then dry it once more with the head bent forward, drying and brushing against the direction of growth.

• The advantage of both methods is that the hair acquires more body, especially the hair at the back of the head. The top layer of hair which usually receives more abuse from rough combing etc, is also protected.

• It is important to hold the hairdryer in such a way that the air blows from the root to the ends. Only in this way does the hair's scaly layer remain smooth and the hair really shines.

Left: using a skeleton brush and a dryer you can give a lot of body to a straight hairline. Roll the hair over the brush and blow warm air on to it with the dryer

• When using the hairdryer always hold it far enough away – there should be about 20 centimetres between the nozzle and the hair. The lesser the distance, the higher the temperature on most dryers. This does not happen with hairdryers with a sensor.

Blow-drying over a brush

Drying the hair over a blow-dryer brush – brushing or air styling – is ideal for short or medium-length straight hair or hair which is slightly wavy. The hair gains more volume, elasticity and movement. Suitable brushes are skeleton brushes and round brushes (see also page 79). Using a round brush with a narrow diameter or an electric dryer brush (an air styler) you can also create curls with short to medium-length hair.

For long hair, brushing or air styling is not really suitable. The procedure takes a lot of time and the lift and curls created are soon lost.

It is best to proceed as follows:

• Work through the hair with a brush when it is already medium dry. As long as the hair is still soaking wet your attempts at styling will produce nothing.

• Begin with the lower part of the hair, and clip the rest on to the crown. In this way you will prevent strands that are still wet coming into contact with those which are already shaped and dry.

• Work from the roots, pulling each individual strand with light tension over the brush and against the direction of growth. Repeat this procedure until the strand is quite dry.

• Depending on the strength of the hair, it is possible to achieve a more or less curly effect, by using a thin, round brush, especially if the strands to be dried are wrapped around the brush; direct the warm air on to it. With a larger brush it is possible to get some curl into the ends and more lift at the hairline.

• Very important: first dry each strand with warm air and then turn the dryer on to cold air. If the dryer has no cold air setting, leave the brush in the hair for a moment until it has cooled off a little. By doing so more tension is put into the hair.

Easy and casual: finger styling

● Short hair will get more lift and increased volume if styling mousse is applied to medium-dry hair at the hairline. Then go through the hair with the fingers spread apart; take hold of the ends and pull them away from the head. Now blow-dry. Finally close the hand and lightly scrunch the ends.

● Scrunched curls demand a little patience, but look casual. Take a little styling mousse and knead it into the hair. Then grab the hair with the hands, press the strands lightly together and blow into the hollow of the hands.

What to look for when buying a hairdryer

Modern hairdryers are power tools – the strongest are up to 2000 watts. The advantage of a powerful dryer is that the more powerful the stream of air, the lower the temperature can be. And that is good for hair – a sensitive natural material.

High wattage, however, should not be the only criterion when buying a hairdryer. Other considerations are often more important. For example:

● Does the dryer feel good to hold, and are the switches easy to operate?

● Is it light enough, so that with prolonged use you do not get tired?

● Is it quiet?

● Is the cable joined to the dryer and made in such a way that it does not become tangled?

You should also consider what the hairdryer is to be used for:

● Just for drying? If so, for long or strong hair a dryer with a high wattage is recommended. This will save you a lot of time. For fine hair, which in any case dries more easily, a less powerful dryer is perfectly adequate.

● For drying and styling? Then you should buy a dryer with a choice of three temperature levels: a high setting for pre-drying, a medium setting for styling, and a cool setting for cooling off styled strands. Dryers with brushes that can be attached, converting the dryer into an air-styler are a sensible option to consider if you will be doing a lot of styling.

● For drying permanent waves a diffuser attachment is useful. This giant nozzle turns the air-stream into a gentle flow that does not blow the hair about and protects the curls.

● For travelling? A dryer with a folding handle is very practical, as it takes up very little room. A dryer that can be adjusted to different voltages, and has an adaptor set for travelling abroad is probably the most useful.

1 *Curls and fluffy contours can be achieved by twisting the hair around a round brush and blow-dried. Strands already dried should be cooled off using either the cold air or twisting around the finger, then pin them up and leave to cool.*

2 *To give lift to short hair, pull the hair upwards and blow dry. With fine hair, first use some setting lotion and finish with hairspray.*

3 *For masculine looking cuts, finger styling is usually sufficient: first knead styling mousse into the hair, then using open fingers pull the hair backwards. The shape will stay best if afterwards the hair is not combed again.*

4 *Anyone who likes to experiment with styling should have a small collection of brushes: two round brushes for different types of curls, and a half-round brush for shape and volume.*

5 *A good hairdryer is vital. The most modern equipment offers a higher wattage and different strengths of air flow, which can be combined with any temperature required (from cold to hot). A rotary handle that alleviates wrist strain because it can be moved to any position is a boon.*

6 *A dryer with a diffuser is recommended for use on naturally curly and permed hair. It only blows gently and is not very hot, so you can get close up to the hair.*

USING ELECTRIC STYLERS

Warm air styler or curling tongs: how do they differ?

What can each do particularly well?

How often can they be used?

Modern electric stylers lift flat hairlines and give life to limp ends. Two completely different types are available:

● A hot-air brush, which has short, round plastic bristles and jets in between that blow the air into the hair (not to be confused with hot-air curlers). Wet and dry hair can be styled with it.

● Combi curling tongs work in the same way as classical curling tongs and are equipped with a warm-up system. These are only suitable for dry hair. They are available with a shiny metal surface, coated, or – like the hot air brush – with bristles.

Left: curling tongs. The diameter of the brush can be changed to five different sizes simply by turning the handle. Far right: combi-styler with removable brush that can also be used to pre-dry the hair

Brush or smooth tongs?

Brush stylers are somewhat easier to use. They grasp the hair better, and the strands are easier to roll up. In the case of long hair, where the ends are rather rough, they have a small disadvantage: when unrolling the hair it tangles easily in the bristles – even when the appliance has an automatic roller. To avoid this, the strands have to be kept carefully apart. They must not be too thickly or too tightly wound around the brush.

Not so much care is required when using smooth curling tongs. Some practice is required to ensure that the strands are rolled up smoothly and the ends are not broken. A classical smooth set of tongs enables ringlets to be made much more easily, as its diameter is considerably thinner than the brush head's.

If your hairstyle changes frequently, it is a good idea to have curlers with many different heads.

What you must always remember when using a styler:

Electric stylers are a really practical invention. If possible, they should not be used every day as over time the dry heat can make the hair brittle.

It is essential to take very good care of your hair; the ends, in particular, need regular treatment. It is a good idea before styling to put a little hair cream on to the sensitive ends for protection. If your hair already has gel, setting mousse or spray in it, electric stylers should not be used. Otherwise the hair will become hard and sticky, and the end result will not turn out as you would wish.

PERFECT CURLING

If your curls are to keep their shape but look as natural as possible, the best things to use are rollers.

This is the best way to wind the hair on rollers:

● As with hot-air styling, the hair should first be dried a little then you can begin to put the damp but not wet hair into the rollers. The remaining moisture will be sufficient to bring the required tension to the hair and also shortens the drying time.

● Beside the rollers, you will also need a narrow-toothed comb with a handle, to divide the strands and a spray bottle with water to moisten again the parts of the hair that have already dried. It is also useful to have a second mirror so that you can see the position of the rollers at the back of the head.

● The divided strands of hair should be narrower than the width of the roller. Only hair that sits exactly on the rollers will gain the required tension. Each strand should, if possible, be rolled vertically to the scalp so that the rollers lie exactly over the hair roots and not diagonally alongside. This would also cause the hair to lose some of its spring.

● The firmer the position of the rollers, the tighter the tension of the whole hair. To

Left: foam rollers are easy to use. The hair is easy to roll up because the ends cling well to the round surface

achieve this pull the strand a little way away from the head before rolling up; it should not, however, be so tight that it pulls.

● The rollers should be fastened in such a way that there are no kinks. This can occur when the rollers have rubber bands or clips. There is less risk with rollers that are held in place with plastic pins or hair pins.

● Always insert the pins against the direction in which the hair has been rolled; the end should be anchored in the previous roller. (In the case of the first roller over the forehead, the end of the pin should be on the scalp.)

● Work from front to back when putting the rollers in, beginning in the middle of the head.

● With long hair the strands should not be too thick, otherwise they take too long to dry.

● Short hair that can easily slip out of the rollers should be 'lengthened' with curl papers. This makes rolling easier.

● Fine hair should first be sprayed with setting lotion. This gives the style lift. But be careful – only weak lotions are really suitable for fine hair.

Very curly or straight – the rollers determine the effect

● For small curls that are to last a long time, fairly thin rollers are needed. A really curly, fuzzy head is achieved with perm curlers.

● Medium-sized rollers in medium-length hair produce generous curls; in long hair cut level they produce soft waves. In short hair they produce only volume and bounce.

● Large rollers produce no curls, but make the hair puff out and give bounce to the ends. They are suitable for medium-length and long hair.

● Small rollers bring a lot of tension to the hair and produce especially bushy curls and waves (see also page 104).

With such large rollers you will not get any curls, but much more volume

Tips for drying and styling

• Single rollers (eg for providing more volume at the back of the head) can be dried with a normal hairdryer. With a head completely covered in rollers, using a hairdryer is too tiring – it is worth buying a hood dryer. Modern appliances operate with one or two blowers which blow warm air into inflating plastic sections. The plastic hood rests gently against the curlers and is hardly felt. It is also not necessary with these hoods to remain sitting near an electric socket. Extended cables allow for relatively free movement.

Dryers with a cool setting are best, so that the hair can be brought down to a normal temperature again before the rollers are removed.

• The dry hair should be thoroughly cool before the rollers are removed, because as a result of the warmth, the keratin becomes soft and must become hard again if it is to retain its new shape. Depending on the thickness of the rolled strands, it takes between five to 10 minutes for the hair to cool down. If you have a dryer with a cool setting you can reduce the cooling time.

• If the hair is rolled on to thin rollers and the intention is to make small curls that fall around the head, it is best to use a wide-toothed comb. After combing, place a little setting mousse on the fingers and pull the curls into shape. To comb the hair, use a comb with a handle or a brush to produce dense curls.

• If no curls are required, just volume and movement, brush the hair thoroughly after removing the rollers. If individual sections or the style as a whole has turned out too curly, pull the strands individually over the brush and blow-dry. Under no circumstances moisten the hair again, or it will lose its tension.

• If the hair fluffs up too much or has turned out curlier than you expected, you can get the shape you want by using styling products. Simply rub a little setting mousse or hair wax between the palms and lightly work into the hair.

1 *A few electric rollers can bring bounce to a straight page-boy style. The hair is rolled up dry, in front on small rollers, at the back on large rollers. After cooling, brush well in all directions and shape with a little gel/wax.*

2 *A tapered cut will have more volume if just the top hair is rolled on large rollers. The simplest way is to use self-fixing rollers; place all around from the parting.*

3 *Large rollers, such as those in the photo, give a page-boy style with a centre parting more fullness.*

4 *Volume in a 60s style can be achieved by placing a few large rollers at the back of the head and back-combing the underside of the strands immediately after drying. Comb the covering hair straight and fix with a spray.*

5 *If long hair is to fall in generous waves, roll the section over the forehead in medium-sized rollers parallel with the parting to right and left. Roll the hair at the back of the head in the direction of the neck. After drying the hair, comb gently through with a wide-toothed comb.*

CURLERS AND CLIPS

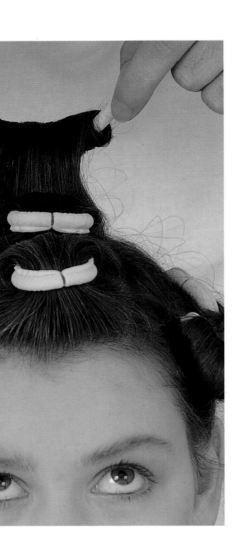

1 *Flexible rollers, or styling rods, are the original form of all rollers and are still useful. They bring a lot of tension to the hair. To use: divide hair into thin strands, lay the ends smoothly over the roller, roll up the hair and bend the ends together. Simply put the rollers halfway up the length of the strand, wrap the outer end around the rod and then roll up to the roots.*

2 *Accurate positioning of these rollers is not necessary. As the waves are particularly narrow, inaccuracies are not obvious.*

3 *Take the rollers out only when the hair is completely dry. As the air does not circulate as well as with ordinary rollers, drying takes longer. For quicker drying either use a drying hood, or dry the hair first and then roll up, moistening the hair with setting lotion only. Incidentally, these rollers will produce especially bushy hair if you twist the individual strands like cords before rolling up.*

In hair all of the same length and cut level, these rollers will produce only soft waves. The more layered the cut, the more curly the locks.

To produce waves on the forehead you can use clips, butterfly clips or special combs. It is not easy to do – it needs a lot of skill and practice.

Points to note: it is easier with natural curls, and the hair must be really damp and strengthened with setting lotion.

1 *Making waves using clips: comb the hair away from the forehead, then, using the edge of the hand, gently push it forwards again. Fix two or three clips behind the resulting wave. Do the same for the next and the following waves.*

2 *Using butterfly clips is the easiest way to make waves: push the hair with the hand towards the roots and fix the butterfly clips exactly on the peak of the waves.*

3 *Making waves with little combs: ideal for natural waves that are supposed to be large over the forehead. Comb the hair back and push a comb in front and behind each wave as it forms.*

For all three techniques: let the hair dry properly, or blow dry, then spray with a strong setting lotion and very carefully remove clips, or combs. Do not comb through the waves.

1

2

3

WHAT GIVES THE HAIR SHAPE?

Mousse, gel, setting lotion, spray and wax all make styles last longer, and some would not be possible at all without these products. But which are suitable for which purpose?

Styling products are some of the best selling items among hair cosmetics. One thing most have in common is that they all contain what is known as 'film formers'. These are usually synthetic resins that build up in the hair and make it thicker and firmer. Styling aids do not damage the hair. Anyone who thinks their hair is being damaged will most likely find that they are using the wrong product for their hair type, or are using too much of the right one. The amount used is crucial for achieving the desired effect.

Setting lotions

These always make the hair a little harder so it binds together better. They protect the hair from the heat of the hair dryer and from air moisture, and give the style more volume and shape.

● Liquid setting lotions are very practical. They can be sprayed on or work well if applied from a bottle containing enough for a single application. They can be evenly applied and should be used sparingly.

Left: for curls that need plenty of structure, work in a handful of styling mousse and leave it to dry on its own; do not comb

● Liquid setting lotions are also known as 'brushing lotions'; they help give blow-dried styles a little support without reducing the lift produced by the dryer.

● Setting lotions with strong setting characteristics are suitable for styles that have been created with rollers.

● With colour setting lotions, your hair colour can be changed, varied or intensified, from wash to wash. With the exception of bleaches, these lotions can be completely washed out afterwards.

● As a rule, all liquid setting lotions are designed for use on wet hair. If you want to freshen the hair up quickly, however, the setting lotion can also be applied to dry hair for a change. Do it like this: lightly spray individually divided strands, roll on to a round brush or larger rollers, and quickly blow-dry. The hair will hold its new position and tension.

● Styling mousse is a little different from the liquid lotions, but its effect, giving the hair shape and firmness, is very similar. Also called foaming mousse, it is suitable for use on dry as well as wet hair.

● Styling mousse is ideal for curly styles that can be kneaded into shape with the fingers. As setting mousse contains very little moisture, but makes the hair easy to shape, the hair can first be blow-dried until almost dry and then the mousse worked in. If the styling effect is to be particularly striking, the hair should not be combed again afterwards.

● How much mousse is required depends largely on the length and thickness of the hair. For short to chin-length hair, a blob as large as a mandarin is usually enough. For thick and long hair, twice or three times as much will be needed. Tip for use: apply the required amount in small single portions. Apply the mousse to the palms and knead into the hair a little at a time.

1 *This is the proper way to apply styling mousse: place a small amount in the palm, and work well into the wet hair. Repeat until all the hair has been coated. Then blow-dry. Useful tip: after drying the hair, work in a little setting mousse, so that the style is accentuated.*

2 *Short hair can be styled using fixing gel. Rub some gel between the fingers, and beginning at the roots, twist into small strands.*

3 *A good styling spray gives the hair shape, without making it too stiff.*

4 *Styling gel is available in different types: 'firm' for a firm hold, and 'wet' for a wet look and lighter hold.*

5 *Wax gives the hair a brilliant gloss, but does not hold it.*

6 *By back-combing, the hair is lifted upwards in strands and then, using a fine-tooth back-combing comb from behind, is pushed in the direction of the roots. This creates volume, but does roughen the surface of the hair if done continuously. Important: the hair should be carefully combed straight before going to bed.*

7 *Styles that are supposed to look wet are combed into shape with wet-look gel. Ideal for severe styles such as the 'garçon look'.*

Gel – for wet-look styles

These styling tips are only suitable for dry hair.

● Wet gel does not as a rule set the hair very strongly, but gives it a wet-looking gloss. All of the hair can be treated in this way and then styled close to the head. Another possibility to emphasise different parts of the head, for example, is to make a forehead wave or have just curly wet ends. Optimum results can be achieved with wet gel with thick dark hair. Fine ash blonde hair looks a little pathetic and very light hair looks a little streaky and scruffy.

● Styling gel is a stronger styling product that has a less emphasised wet look. It is useful for hairline waves, short hedgehog spikes and fringes that stand upright. It is important to know that styling gel makes the hair somewhat harder – the larger the amount used, the more so. With fine hair, use only sparingly.

For shine and structure: wax and cream

Hair wax gives the hair a beautiful gloss and a little more shape. Straight hair looks more compact; curls will be more defined. In contrast with treatment with gel, the hair does not stick together in strands, assuming, of course, that the correct amount has been used - in this case always use sparingly.

How to use: rub a little wax between the palms to make it smooth, then spread over the surface of the hair or work into the curls.

Hair wax is ideal, above all, for close cropped hair, to control bushy natural or permed waves, and for straightening curls that are too tight – in this case it can also be used for fine hair. However, it usually makes fine hair too heavy and limp.

● A hybrid product is gel-wax, with which similar effects can be achieved. It is softer than wax, however, and therefore simpler to use.

● 'Structure' cream is a cross between setting lotion and wax. It provides gloss, defines hair structures and gives a light hold to the hair.

Hair spray – the strong classic

This is the 'oldie' among styling preparations, but it is still widely used and is indispensable for many styles. The variation, hair lacquer, provides extra strong setting power and is still fashionable. The days have gone, however, when hair spray produced stiff, accurately styled curls and back-combed towers of hair, a kind of frozen 'polyester look'. Today it is used sparingly and in many different ways.

● Hair rolled on curlers often needs only a little hair spray as a styling aid. After brushing the hair thoroughly, shake it, spray all round and dry –for a short time. Then comb the hair into shape and finally fix with a little spray again. In this way, the style will maintain a good shape which will last. A spray of medium strength is best for this purpose.

● Fine, long hair is best sprayed with the head bent forward and the hair hanging over the face. This gives the hair underneath more lift, leaving the covering hair manageable and able to be styled.

● Straight hair acquires greater volume very quickly when different strands are held away from the head and the hairline only is sprayed. Here, also, a medium spray is right.

● For a standing fringe, a strong spray is best. Fringe hair should be lightly back-combed from the back, combed straight forward and then sprayed.

● Hair spray is also ideal for stabilising fine, flyaway hair. Do not use a strong spray because this would only make the hair stiff. For this purpose, the best spray is a 'light' strength. Spray lightly, leave to dry and style as usual.

CHAPTER 5

For every taste:
WAVES
for a change

- The secret of permanent waving

- How wavy should it be

- Are 'acid' waves better?

- How to stop waves looking limp

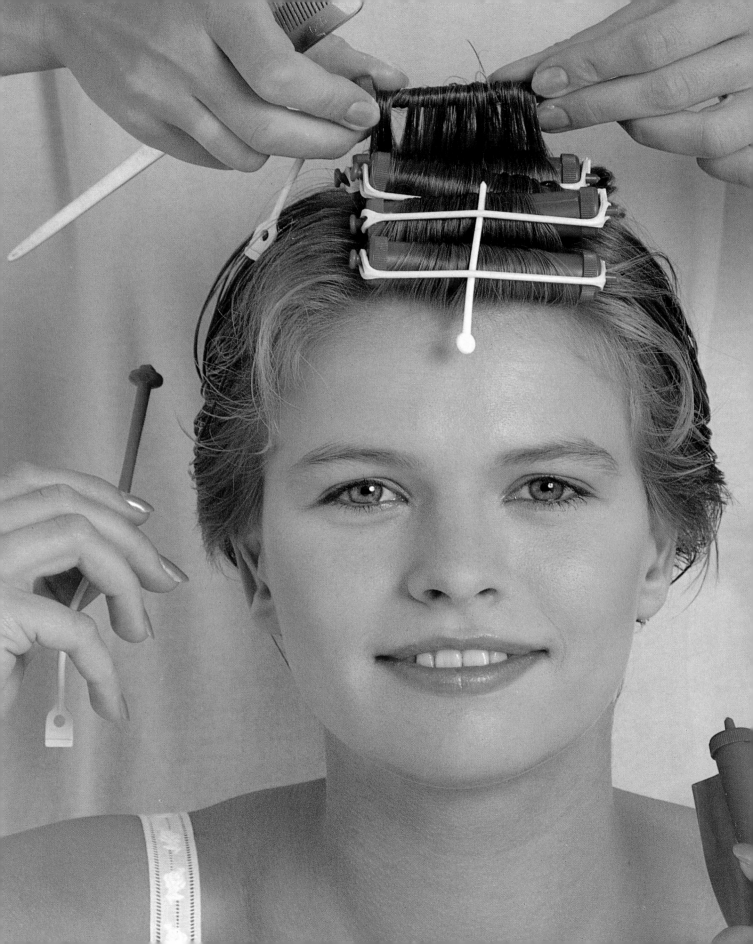

ALL ABOUT PERMS

A perm will help thin, smooth hair achieve more volume and magnificent waves, but it does not refresh the hair.

There is no other technique that can do so much for the appearance of plain hair, but with nothing else can so much go wrong. A perm is a far-reaching chemical intervention into the structure of the hair that is practically impossible to reverse. Anyone thinking of a perm should consider the following:

• The perm technique must be absolutely suitable for the hair type, its condition and the style itself. Perms should therefore only be carried out by a hairdresser who is conversant both with the hair and the client's personal taste.

• The first consideration should be what is wanted – small curls, generous waves, close waves, soft waves, or no curls or waves at all but simply more bounce and volume. The best thing to do is to collect photos that will show the hairdresser quite clearly what the result should look like.

• Every perm makes a hairstyle look centimetres shorter. Straight hair just to the shoulder can, as a result of

Left: the position and size of the rollers when perming determine the fall of the waves. The client should discuss this very fully with the hairdresser

being waved, shrink to chin length. In addition, damaged ends must be trimmed before or after the perm.

• Important: the result of the perm will depend very much on the cut. Real curls are only formed when the hair is layered. Long hair should be cut level.

• Without care and attention no permanent wave will look pretty for an extended period of time.

• Last, but not least, it is wrong to believe that a perm makes styling unnecessary. Only in the case of tight curls is this achieved by drying alone. Soft curls, on the other hand, must nearly always be brought into shape with rollers and curling tongs. However, the hair will have much more shape than straight hair.

How a permanent wave works

A perm works in three stages, each requiring a great deal of care:

The first stage:

The wave liquid penetrates to the interior of the hair, and opens what is known as the sulphur bridge (ie the chemical structures which give the hair its stability). This makes the hair soft and malleable. The chemical substance used in the classical alkaline wave

preparations is called 'thioglycol'. In the case of acid wave preparations 'thioglycolester' is used. It is especially important in the first stage that the wave liquid and the time it is left on is precisely suitable for the type of hair being treated. A wave preparation that is too weak and a setting time that is too short make the perm too weak; it will therefore not hold so well. A preparation that is too strong and left on for too long can destroy the structure of the hair.

The second stage:

The fibre layer softened by the wave preparation takes on the shape of the rollers a little at a time. The hairdresser must always check this process. He or she checks the changing shape by unrolling a test roller twice and looking at the effect on the roots, the healthiest part of the hair. Using the correct type and size of rollers is vital. They are decisive in the appearance of the perm – and also make it last. The thinner the roller, the smaller, curlier and longer lasting the perm will be. The thicker the roller, the more generous the waves will be, but the quicker they may become limp.

The third stage:

When the wave medium has done its work, it must be thoroughly rinsed out. With a normal perm, this must be at least three minutes; with acid perms at least five minutes. The reason is that if the hair is not rinsed thoroughly enough and traces of the perm remain, the process continues. The result is damage to the hair and lack of durability. After the hair has been rinsed, it will have changed its shape and yet will still be soft. Finally comes what is known as 'fixing' or neutralising when a hydrogen peroxide solution is applied. It closes the 'sulphur bridge' mentioned at the beginning and makes the hair stable again.

It is especially important that the neutraliser is applied with great care, evenly over every hair, otherwise the perm will not hold.

Are acid perms better than alkaline ones?

At one time 'acid' perms were considered mild. This is no longer necessarily the case. Constituents and effects have changed, so both types now have advantages and disadvantages.

Acid perm preparations protect the hair more, because the substance is not absorbed as readily by the hair and it does not swell so much. However, the resulting waves are not as durable as those from alkaline preparations. There is also a risk of allergic reactions from using acid wave preparations, although they are suitable for most people.

Today's classic alkaline permanent wave is not anything like as aggressive as it once was, due mainly to special additives in the perm solution - for example, chlorophylin, a derivative of leaves that supports the waving process, or so-called 'active' care substances and panthenol, that repair existing hair damage and prevent waving from being too aggressive.

As a general rule:

Alkaline wave preparations are advantageous for hair that is difficult to wave, for healthy hair, and with hair styles for which a medium to strong, and above all durable, wave result is required.

Acid wave preparations are particularly important for gentle changes, for long and for previously waved hair, or strongly bleached hair.

Should you perm your own hair?

This is a sensitive question. Theoretically and practically there should be no problem. Preparations are available everywhere and their quality is not necessarily any worse than those available in salons. Many women use these with great success. However, remember that a home perm cannot be as precise or as well matched to your hair quality as one carried out by a good hairdresser. He or she has professional knowledge and the necessary experience.

Right: what happens during a permanent wave? If you know exactly what happens you will not be easily alarmed. This is the process in a few words:

1 *Diagnosis of the hair and choice of suitable waving preparation.*

2 *Roller and rolling technique must be absolutely right for the desired result.*

3 *The perm solution is applied to the individual rollers.*

4 *Warmth supports the wave process.*

5 *The hairdresser checks the wave result at the roots.*

6 *Then the basic waving preparation must be thoroughly rinsed out.*

7 *Final drying is necessary, so the neutraliser can work.*

8 *Using a sponge, the neutraliser is applied to the hair. It makes the new shape stable.*

9 *Now the rollers must come out. It is fixed once more, then rinsed – and the process is complete.*

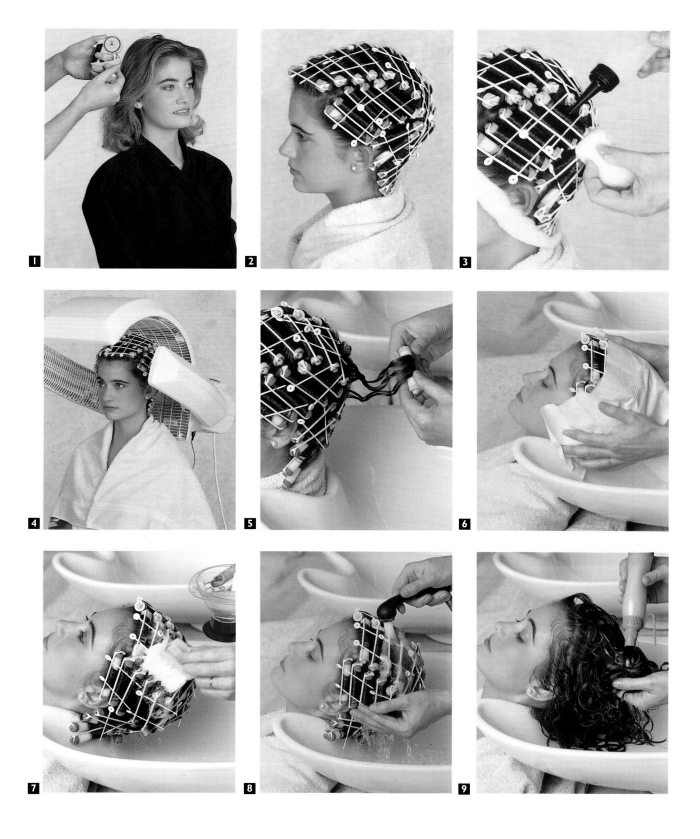

Therefore anyone with relatively short, healthy hair, with no particular style in mind, and who has a friend to help with the rollers can be successful at home. However, it is important to follow the instructions for use precisely. Someone who has definite ideas about the style they want, or someone with special hair problems (eg highlighted, dyed, already waved hair, long or damaged hair) should go to the hairdresser.

Permanent waves and colour – will the hair stand both?

Creating permanent waves and colouring the hair do not cancel each other out, but they should not be undertaken at the same time. Professionals recommend having a perm first, and two to three weeks afterwards having the hair dyed. Immediately after a perm, however, the hair can be toned. Often it is a good idea, as freshly permed hair is often somewhat pale in colour, and toning can bring more brilliance and a lovely gloss to the hair.

Making hair blonde, as opposed to going darker, creates problems for permed hair. Only hair that is naturally strong will stand a change of colour as well as a permanent wave. The second condition is that the hair must not be too long.

Gentle lightening, on the other hand, is possible in the case of weaker and permed hair, but only if a lot of care is given afterwards.

Creating permanent waves with highlights involves a rather complicated procedure. Here hair that has been subject to chemical treatment and hair in its natural condition grow side by side. The differing hair qualities must be waved in totally different ways which, of course, is not possible. The solution: a special pre-treatment, in which the blonde strands are strengthened and protected. Perms applied to highlighted hair must only be undertaken by a hairdresser.

What should you do if the permanent wave slowly grows out?

A first perm usually turns out very well indeed – as long as the hairdresser has done his or her work well, and there has been previous agreement on the intended result. However, what should you do when the hair grows and the new hair lies flat on top of the head, while the rest is still curly?

With relatively short hair, the problem can be solved by a trim that takes account of the remaining perm until eventually all the old waves have been cut out. It is a little more difficult with long hair that is to remain long. If the hair is fairly strong and has

been well looked after, it may well stand a second perm, but certainly not a third. With fine or damaged hair, there will be all kinds of hidden risks with a second perm.

The solution is a 'root perm', where the ends are not put in rollers at all, or are previously treated and therefore protected by this procedure, so they will hardly be affected by a second perm. In the case of a root perm, it is very important that the strength of the perm must be measured against the remainder of the previous perm to create a harmonious overall look. For this reason, a root perm is best done in the same salon and by the same hairdresser as the original perm.

Tip: root perms are also ideal when the hair needs a bit of life putting back into it, but the rest of the hair is to be left untouched. The permed roots will grow with time, but the reshaping should last for approximately three months and have a positive effect when blow-drying and styling.

These days it is possible to achieve many different effects with perms

1 *A quite light perm using large rollers will give fine short hair more bounce and volume. For styling, use setting mousse applied with the fingers.*

2 *A 'volume perm' is also obtained by using large rollers. So that the hair looks fluffy and falls straight, it should be styled with a dryer and brush.*

3 *A 'part perm' in which just the top and back of the head are rolled in medium rollers. Casual waves result if the hair is styled with curling tongs.*

4 *To produce body waves, the hair must first be wedge cut, otherwise it falls into curls. After washing, comb with a wide-toothed comb and knead into shape with styling mousse.*

5 *For a long mane of curls such as this a thick, level cut is required, along with a lot of patience when carrying out the perm. In this case, many hairdressers use flexible rollers, curl papers or spiral rollers.*

6 *A perm rolled on medium rollers will put soft curls and body into fine hair. Style the ends using curling tongs, gently flexing into the desired shape.*

1

2

3

4

5

6

LOOKING AFTER WAVES

So that the shine and bounce are retained, a perm must be given good care and treatment. Follow these very important tips.

Good hairdressers will give their customers one or two good tips as they leave the salon for home.

• A fresh permanent wave should, if possible, be left alone on the first day – do not comb or brush. Sometimes this is difficult to resist. Despite this, however, you should follow this rule without exception. The reason: the hair keratin will still be somewhat soft, and not all 'sulphur bridges' (see page 113) will have completely closed. Until this has happened, avoid any unnecessary stretching of the hair. Follow these rules and you will be much happier with the perm later on.

• The perm should only be washed on the third day. The reason is the same as for the combing restriction, as in its wet, swollen state, the hair is especially sensitive. Also avoid curling tongs, rollers and brush-dryers. The more care taken with the hair at this time, the longer the perm will remain looking good.

Perms that have been left to dry naturally and have not formed proper curls again, can be sprayed with water (using a fine houseplant spray), or with a special spray, to refresh the curls.

Tips on everyday care

• Hair that has been permed should always be washed with great care. A 'root wash' is ideal: dilute the shampoo with water and apply to wet hair with a spray bottle. When rinsing, the shampoo spreads throughout the rest of the hair and is sufficient to clean the hair thoroughly. Permed hair does not necessarily have to be washed every day. Usually this is not necessary, as the hair will have become a little more porous and will have absorbed more grease from the head.

• To untangle a wet perm use a comb with wide teeth. Avoid any pulling and tugging.

• Use a wide-toothed comb for dry hair too and, if using a brush, it should be a skeleton brush with rounded plastic teeth.

• Avoid anything that dries the hair out – direct sun, salt or chlorinated water, or strong wind. If sunbathing always wear a headscarf or hat; after swimming rinse the hair well; and when driving in an open car do not forget to wear a headscarf or a hat.

• In addition, the hair should be left to dry naturally whenever possible, or use a hairdryer with a diffuser. This will blow air very gently and protect the hair whilst drying.

Special preparations that you should always have available:

• An extra-mild shampoo with gentle ingredients.

• A conditoner or spray treatment to care for the hair after washing, so that the comb can pass through the hair without snagging.

• A correct hair treatment to use after every third or fourth wash.

• For long hair, a split end treatment, to protect against damage to the ends.

You will find most of these products for permed hair generally available. They are recommended especially for fine hair. The repair substances they contain strengthen the hair structure, but are also so light that the waves and curls do not become unduly heavy and will therefore keep their shape.

CHAPTER 6

For everyone – self help: small corrections with

SCISSORS

- Careful – you are not the hairdresser!

- The correct tools for the job

- Cutting the fringe – but not too much

- Shortening the sides

- Just trim the ends, please!

CUTTING HAIR YOURSELF

Cutting hair is really easy for the professional hairdresser. But almost every woman occasionally reaches for the scissors - usually with very doubtful results.

Who has not had this experience: you look in the mirror and think 'How dreadful!' The fringe is too long, the top hair is falling apart, the sides are growing over the ears. Yesterday everything looked all right. Gentle panic sets in as the next appointment with the hairdresser is still two weeks away. But you want to look great today. What can be an easier solution than to reach for the scissors yourself? Here a cut, there a snip – and then it is already too late. The hair is certainly shorter, but the shape no better than before.

Usually you reach the conclusion – never again! Nevertheless, good resolutions are seldom kept, so here are a few tips for the day when you next get irresistibly itchy fingers.

● Take your time. Any corrections made in a hurry at home, or during a coffee break at work, are bound to fail.

● Cut only those places that you can see well. This is difficult enough, even using a mirror.

Small hair scissors with teeth which are scarcely visible are ideal for non-professionals. The right comb is made of india-rubber or zinc, which will hold the strands of hair firmly

● It is better to ask a friend, sister or mother for help. (The cutting instructions on the following pages are meant for them.)

● Cutting the hair when wet is the way the professionals do it, but it is easy to cut too much off. This does not happen so easily if the hair is dry, but then the strands are more difficult to grasp. Try out both to see which works best.

● If you are cutting a child's hair, it is important that they sit still; moving around with scissors is a dangerous business. The child should be distracted with a book or a story cassette.

Very important: use professional scissors and the correct comb. When cutting, do not use normal household scissors or scissors for cutting paper. There are special scissors for cutting hair obtainable from every hairdressing product supplier. These professional scissors can be easily recognised, as they are ground in a special way so that the hair is cut cleanly. With most other scissors, the hair will be broken or bent.

Professional scissors:

● with tiny teeth on both blades

● 'modelling scissors', with large teeth on one blade

● 'thinning scissors', with large teeth on both blades

For amateurs only those with tiny teeth on both blades are necessary; the modelling and thinning scissors are unnecessary.

So that the hair does not slip through the teeth of the comb when you are cutting it, you should buy a proper hair cutting comb from a hairdressing product supplier. It will be 15 to 18 cm long, made from natural material (india-rubber or horn), and have conical teeth with rounded points.

CUTTING THE FRINGE

Shorten the fringe – in an emergency

you can do it yourself. But beware:

wet hair gets shorter as it dries!

1 *Make the wet fringe v-shaped and comb into the face; tie the rest of the hair back.*

2 *Using the fingertips push the fringe hair gently backwards and forwards. This will show if there is a crown anywhere. If this is the case, cutting must begin at this point.*

3 *Divide a section approximately two centimetres wide diagonally across the forehead and comb into the face. Clip back the rest with hairclips, and dampen the front part of the fringe again. Comb a four-centimetre section straight, clamp the section between your forefinger and middle finger, and pull tightly downwards. When doing so, the middle finger should have contact with the skin of the face. (If there are crowns in the hair, hold the section a little less tightly.) Now cut off the ends – but not too much! When wet the fringe should be two centimetres longer than the desired length. It will 'shrink' on its own when dried. Now shorten the hair to right and left of the first section to the same length; use a little of the already shortened hair between your fingers as a measure.*

4 *The hair that has been clipped back should now be combed over the hair which has already been cut.*

5 *Take the single sections between the fingers again, pull downwards and cut the ends. Measure them against the already shortened fringe hair.*

6 *If necessary, finally snip off any odd lengths with the scissors – first while the fringe is wet, then when dry.*

CUTTING SIDEBOARDS

A tip: if only the top and hair at the back is to be longer than the rest, occasionally shorten the sides.

1 Comb the wet hair in such a way that it lies in the natural direction of growth.

2 Cut off the lower part of the hair diagonally. The parting here should be at the height of the eyebrows and upper ear. Clip the upper hair.

3 Take the lower section between the forefinger and middle finger and pull downwards. (The middle finger should touch the surface of the face.) Cut the ends diagonally to the ear.

4 Loosen the hair that was clipped up, divide some hair from a higher parting and clip on top. Comb this newly parted hair over that which has already been cut. From front to back take a section through the fingers one after the other, pull lightly diagonally towards the front and cut off the upper ends, taking the length from those underneath. Follow the shape of the ear. If necessary, repeat everything again, making an even higher parting.

5 Fold the ear and hold tightly. Comb the side hair towards the front and cut cleanly from the back to the front.

6 Using the tip of the scissors, make a few last corrections.

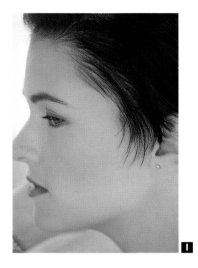

1

2

3

4

5

6

SHORTENING LONG HAIR

Shortening the length of hair is good for geting rid of split ends. This is really something for professionals, but who does not like playing at being a hairdresser?

1 *Work with wet hair. Begin in the neck. Just above the ear lobes make a parting across the back of the neck and pin up the hair above the parting. The lower hair should be combed straight. Begin cutting in the centre: grasp the ends of the hair between the forefinger and middle finger, pull tightly downwards and cut it horizontally. Now clamp the strands alongside the hair which has already been cut and equalise the lengths. Repeat this for as long as necessary to achieve hair of equal length.*

2 *At the back of the head – a hand's width above the parting – make a completely new parting, and comb the hair straight over the already trimmed hair. Anything protruding should now be snipped away horizontally with the scissors. Important: carefully comb the hair straight before every cut.*

3 *Comparing the length: take the side hair (while holding the head straight) between the fingers, pull straight and compare with the hair in the centre.*

4 *Loosen the rest of the hair and in the way described above adjust with the hair in the centre.*

5 *and* **6** *Comparing the hair length at the front: take the two strands, left and right, between the fingers and pull tight, then compare one with the other. If necessary, correct.*

TRIMMING CURLS

You can also trim a head covered with curls yourself from time to time. As soon as you have grasped the idea, it can be a lot of fun!

1 *Moisten the hair well.*

2 *Part the hair down the centre and comb straight. Take the ends between the forefinger and middle finger, pull tight and trim. In this way, all the hair all around the head should be shortened and the basic length established. When doing this, always take between the fingers a section of the hair already cut with the untrimmed hair. This principle is to be used throughout the whole of the cut.*

3 *Make two partings right and left on the top of the head (with the centre between the eyes). The hair between the partings should be twisted round the finger and clipped up.*

4 *Now cut the hair slowly from the bottom to the top. Use the basic length set at the beginning as a measure and trim any hair longer than this. Take adjacent sections of hair and make the ends the same length. When doing so, pull the strands alternately downwards, forwards, backwards and upwards, so that after drying the hair is round in shape. Take the hair in front of the ears downwards, and behind the ears diagonally upwards, to compare length.*

5 *Unclip the hair from the centre of the head and continue cutting in the way already described.*

6 *Finally, cut any hair that is out of shape with the scissors.*

SUITABLE PRODUCTS

In the first five chapters of this book you have read all about hairstyles and hair care.

Here are some more tips

Tips on Chapter 1

Colouring and toning are best left to the professionals. Wella products are used by hairdressing salons throughout the country. For an introduction to colour, Wella's Colourfresh range comprises semi-permanent conditioning colours which wash out after several shampoos. Colour Touch has longer lasting conditioning hair colours which gradually wash away after 12 shampoos. Koleston 2000 Colour Balsam is a comprehensive range of permanent colours in a gentle balsam base, and Koleston 1+2 Lightening is a gentle blonde colour, ideal for highlights.

Tips on Chapter 2

Choose your hairdresser carefully. Whatever style you decide on, you need a good hairdresser with expert knowledge and skill to make that choice a reality. However, any style is only as good as your skill in managing it. A hairdresser who gives you the right tips about caring for your hair at home deserves your trust, since they obviously feel responsible for your hair in and out of the salon.

Tips on Chapter 3

This chapter gave you important information about hair care. Always use high quality products on your hair. With these Wella products you can practice the tips in this chapter.

Wella System Professional is a comprehensive range of products, available from salons for use at home. There are over 30 products to choose from, which cater for all hair types and any hair or scalp problems - shampoos, scalp treatments, products to treat dry, damaged, coloured and permed hair, and styling products. The range cleanses, conditions, revitalises and protects the hair. Wella System Professional Suncare range comprises products specially formulated to care for and protect your hair while on holiday, and includes shampoo, spray conditioner and spray-on gel.

Wella Lifetex and Lifetex Sun are a range of shampoos and conditioners for salon and home use, also available from salons throughout the country.

Tips on Chapter 4

Wella's System Professional home use products offer a wide choice of special styling products for all styles and types of hair - voluminising spray, styling spray or gel, texture mousse, protection fluid and hairsprays (some refillable, to save money, packaging and the environment).

Wella's High Hair range, also available from salons for home use, offers high performance styling and finishing products. Styling aids include sprays, mousses, gels, wax and clear shine polish. For special effects High Hair's specialist range includes pomades, curl maximiser, wet-look gel and shine cream.

Tips for Chapter 5

Only a professional hairdresser, with training and experience, can decide which permanent wave is best for individual hair, and what effect will result from various perming methods and preparations. Wella's range includes Lockwell, a long-lasting acid perm which produces beautifully conditioned curls on any hair type or texture. Riva is a gentle acid perm with added conditioning properties, and Optaform a gentle conditioning lotion with no-wait neutraliser. Soft and Lasting will produce long lasting curls, even on difficult hair. Styleform Classic, used with perm curlers, produces the movement and volume of natural waves.

ACKNOWLEDGEMENT

The publishers are grateful to Wella Great Britain for the product information on this page. Wella products are available in 150 countries throughout the world. The products mentioned are used by salons throughout the country; Wella System Professional, Lifetex and High Hair can also be purchased from 2,000 salons for use at home. Call Wella GB on 01256 20202, ext. 132, for stockists.

INDEX

Winter colour range

Summer colour range

This is your Magic Colour Swatch. Cut out the pages and use them as instructed to find your colour type.

Autumn colour range

Spring colour range

This is your Magic Colour Swatch. Cut out the pages and use them as instructed to find your colour type.

Autumn

This is your Magic Colour Swatch. Cut out the pages and use them as instructed to find your colour type.

Winter

This is your Magic Colour Swatch. Cut out the pages and use them as instructed to find your colour type.

Summer

This is your Magic Colour Swatch. Cut out the pages and use them as instructed to find your colour type.

Spring

This is your Magic Colour Swatch. Cut out the pages and use them as instructed to find your colour type.

Spring/Autumn

This is your Magic Colour Swatch. Cut out the pages and use them as instructed to find your colour type.

Summer/Winter

This is your Magic Colour Swatch. Cut out the pages and use them as instructed to find your colour type.

Summer

This is your Magic Colour Swatch. Cut out the pages and use them as instructed to find your colour type.

Spring

This is your Magic Colour Swatch. Cut out the pages and use them as instructed to find your colour type.

Spring

This is your Magic Colour Swatch. Cut out the pages and use them as instructed to find your colour type.

Summer

This is your Magic Colour Swatch. Cut out the pages and use them as instructed to find your colour type.

Winter

This is your Magic Colour Swatch. Cut out the pages and use them as instructed to find your colour type.

Autumn

This is your Magic Colour Swatch. Cut out the pages and use them as instructed to find your colour type.

Autumn

This is your Magic Colour Swatch. Cut out the pages and use them as instructed to find your colour type.

Winter

This is your Magic Colour Swatch. Cut out the pages and use them as instructed to find your colour type.